STIGMA

STIGMA

BREAKING THE ASIAN AMERICAN SILENCE ON MENTAL HEALTH

TANAYA KOLLIPARA

NEW DEGREE PRESS

COPYRIGHT © 2021 TANAYA KOLLIPARA

STIGMA

Breaking the Asian American Silence on Mental Health

Cover photograph courtesy of Angelica Shao
Cover models (from left to right): Jenna Siong, Alina Lam, and Maya
Unagi

ISBN   978-1-63730-444-0   *Paperback*
           978-1-63730-545-4   *Kindle Ebook*
           978-1-63730-546-1   *Ebook*

To my parents, my sister, and those who've found themselves drowning in silence for too long. This book was made possible by you all. This book is for you all.

TABLE OF CONTENTS

———

"Mental health is not fight club.
We can talk about it."

—UNKNOWN

NOTE FROM AUTHOR

——

The stories in this book are real.

They come from real people, who decided to share their lived experiences with the world. These individuals have revealed the most intimate details of their lives, in the hope of providing comfort (to those who may be struggling) and promoting empathy (within those hoping to understand mental health better). In doing so, they have provided us with a gift: an opportunity to learn, to understand, to connect, to grow.

The stories I write about in here come explicitly from what the person has decided to share with me; there is no fabrication or falsification. Doing so would be inauthentic, a disservice to the mission of this book—to share people's truths, to remove the stigma around mental health. While these people and their experiences are real, there are many who weren't quite ready to associate their names with their stories. In an effort to preserve their anonymity, some of the names, details, and identifiable information have been changed; in some instances, the events and scenarios of a few interviewed individuals have been culminated into one.

All of these changes were only made after long deliberation, with extreme care taken to ensure the hearts of these stories remained untouched. It is a terrifying place to be in—knowing that the most personal aspects of your life will soon be revealed to the world. So, please understand their need to remain anonymous and my attempts to respect their wishes.

•••

I must also make a note on my use of "Asian American" in the title and in this book.

Throughout the chapters, I will be using "Asian," "Asian American," "AAPI," and "API" interchangeably to reference the Asian American and Pacific Islander racial groups. While doing so is most definitely a disservice to the unique and separate histories of these two groups, it is not without reason.

For one, the majority of research and data lump together Asians and Pacific Islanders into a single monolithic group. This makes it difficult to effectively communicate the findings for the Asian and Pacific Islander groups individually. However, where I can, I will try to reference them as separate entities and share their unique histories. But, ultimately, the focus of my book is on the actual mental health stories and *experiences* of the AAPI community; hence, the information I share *about* these respective communities will be limited. That is why I urge you to look to other sources to learn more.

Secondly, while this is a trivial reason, writing out "Asian American and Pacific Islander" every time will quickly make my writing quite cluttered. Nevertheless, in order to ensure I acknowledge both racial groups, I will prioritize using the terms "AAPI" and "API."

With these explanations, I hope you, my dear reader, can come to understand why I made this decision. My intention is not to erase the distinction between the Asian and Pacific

Islander racial groups. Rather, I aim to make the stories and information as digestible as possible. Only by making the writing clear-cut and accessible can we truly promote greater understanding among *all* members of *all* communities.

CONTENT WARNING

———

The nature of this book deals with sensitive topics, including but not limited to: suicide, mental illness, eating disorders, body dysmorphia, mental health crises/episodes, alcohol and drug abuse, toxic relationships, and self-harm.

This book is filled with the real stories of real people, as they endured their own mental health struggles. While it is inspiring and comforting to read how others overcame (and continue to overcome) their struggles, it is at times taxing—and mentally tiring—to repeatedly read about others' mental traumas. Thus, when reading this book, please be sure to take plenty of breaks, focus on your mental wellness, and pay attention to when you may need to take a step back. Feel free to refer to the "Resources for Further Exploration" section, located at the end of this book, to find tools, websites, groups, and other sources to help you manage your mental health as you read.

As you will soon see, taking these steps to take care of your own mental health is extremely important. Use your support system as a safe space and to have conversations surrounding mental health; utilize your resources as a way to mentally recuperate.

If you ever find yourself contemplating suicide or self-harm, please call your local suicide hotline. Listed below are the hotline numbers of some countries. A more exhaustive list can be found at *opencounseling.com/suicide-hotlines* or by searching "[COUNTRY] suicide hotline" on Google.

United States: (800) 273-8255

Australia: 131114

Barbados: (246) 4299999

Canada: 1 (833) 456-4566

China: 0800-810-1117

France: 0145394000

Ghana: 2332-444-71279

India: 8888817666

Indonesia: 1-800-273-8255

Japan: 810352869090

Malaysia: (06) 2842500

New Zealand: 1737

Philippines: 028969191

Singapore: 1 800 2214444

South Korea: (02) 7158600

Sri Lanka: 011 057 2222662

Thailand: (02) 713-6793

United Kingdom: 08457909090

You must know you are loved, and you are wanted. As you'll soon find, mental illness is something we can live and thrive with. It is simply a part of us; it doesn't make us "less than," nor does it define us.

You are not alone—these stories are evidence of that. There is help out there—I can promise you that.

This is the beginning.

You are opening your heart to be heard, to listen, to heal, and to help. That in itself is a movement of compassion, which will ultimately cause a collective transformation in the climate of care. And slowly, together, we'll create a world that recognizes, prioritizes, and addresses mental health.

INTRODUCTION

——

"I can't breathe."

Wide-eyed, I stared as my friend sank to the kitchen floor, her chest heaving erratically. Although her eyes were squeezed shut, tears made their way down her tan cheeks. Her long, black hair was in a disarray, as her fingers clawed at her scalp. Her lips—which were painted in a deep purple—moved wordlessly, as if in prayer. Except this time, they were praying for mental reprieve.

At fourteen years old, it was a terrifying scene to behold. To walk in and watch as my best friend descended into a panic, unresponsive and unreachable, I did not know what to think. When her head met her knee, I snapped into action. Unsure, I knelt beside her, wrapping my arms around her shoulders. I murmured comforting words, assuring her that she would be alright. Slowly, the shaking subsided, and her breathing became even. A couple of moments later, she lifted her head, her eyes refocused but weary.

I watched, concerned and confused. *What happened? Was something wrong with her? Did anyone else know about this? Did I do the right thing?* These were the questions flying through my mind as my friend wiped her tears and straightened herself. Noticing my face and anticipating my questions, my friend took my hand, gently squeezing.

"Let's talk," she said, her voice still weak from the ordeal.

I later learned my friend had had a panic attack, a byproduct of the severe anxiety and mild paranoia she had been battling for years. While I vaguely knew of her "hurt brain," as her parents would call it, I had never seen how that "hurt" manifested. Whether it was because I was too young to remember or she and her family were too careful to not show me her "weakness," as they believed it to be, this was my first up-close and personal experience with mental illness. Up until that point, I knew very little about the world of mental health; I was only aware of the hushed tones behind closed doors. It was something no one talked about, something that barely existed. It was a source of her shame, a secret her family held in fear of judgment.

In essence, it was her burden—a burden many Asian Americans and Pacific Islanders hold, even today.

Within the broader Asian American community, there is an attitude of fear and disgust toward mental illness and mental health. Due to insufficient understanding and continued misinformation, the AAPI (Asian American and Pacific Islander) community holds a strong sense of judgment toward those with a mental illness. Community members have come to regard these individuals as *lesser-than* and *not-right-in-the-head*. To many, mental illness is seen as a "character defect," a weakness that has to be squashed. As a result, it has become commonplace to hide one's mental health issues in secrecy and in shame. Unsurprisingly, this has created a toxic cycle within the AAPI community. In an effort to hide our mental health struggles, we've completely left them out of the conversation. Without hearing these realities, communities don't develop a sense of empathy with regard to or understanding of mental health.

It's a cycle that is leading to a public health crisis of its own. According to the Substance Abuse and Mental Health Services Administration (SAMHSA), mental health issues are on the rise for API (Asian/Pacific Islander) young adults. In fact, compared to 2008, the rate of mental illness for API adults aged eighteen to twenty-five nearly doubled from 2.9 percent to 5.6 percent by 2018 (United States Department of Health and Human Services, 2018). Even among API youth, the rates of major depressive episodes (MDE) have risen; between 2015 and 2018, the number of youth (age twelve to seventeen) experiencing MDE increased from 10 percent to 13.6 percent. As for older API adults (age twenty-six to forty-nine), surveys have seen an increase in the prevalence of serious mental illness within this subgroup—from 3.2 percent in 2015 to 5 percent in 2018 (Mental Health America, 2021). It's clear to see that, contrary to what many communities want to believe, mental health is becoming increasingly relevant.

In a time when we should be having more conversations surrounding mental health and encouraging the use of resources, API communities in the United States are instead plagued by the stigma of mental health. It has come to a point where it is killing the members of the community: suicide is the *eighth* leading cause of death for Asian Americans and the *first* leading cause of death among API youth (age fifteen to twenty-four) (Hijioka and Wong, 2012; United States Department of Health and Human Services, 2021). To put that into perspective, suicide is only the *eleventh* leading cause of death for all other racial groups combined and the *second* leading cause of death among American youth in general (Centers for Disease Control and Prevention [CDC], 2018; CDC, 2021).

There is a clear need for a renewed focus on mental health and mental illness. The stigma our AAPI communities hold is harming our community members. There needs to be an end to the negative notions carried by many API folks in regard to mental health. All of us, whether we identify as part of the Asian American and Pacific Islander community or not, need to do our part to create an environment where mental health is treated as an important facet of our lives. We need to normalize the use of mental health resources and acknowledge that seeking help is not weak. Alienation should not be the gut reaction to learning about someone's mental health issues. Rather, we should be receiving them with compassion and support.

But to see these changes within the Asian American community, something needs to give. With judgment in the community, few are willing to speak. With few willing to speak, that judgment and stigma are perpetuated. For the vast majority of API individuals, the stigma comes from not knowing these stories. And how can we know, when no one talks about it? For some, it may look like this scary, unknown, invisible entity that doesn't seem to have a cause or much of an effect. We've been taught that it's something people make up for attention, or something that only the "insane" suffer from (and thus we must avoid). But what we may not realize is that mental illness comes in different forms and affects people in different ways. It can have a serious impact on a person's life, but it doesn't warrant isolation or negligence.

After all, I've seen how the lack of understanding and exposure has affected my friend. Her family has seen and experienced how people distanced themselves from them on the rare occasions they spoke about her mental illness. As a result, they've learned to become silent and guarded. While the stigma and the shame may be pervasive, so is the community judgment. The South Asian community, like many other Asian communities, reacted that way because they had not heard the truth about my friend's mental illness. They made their automatic assumptions, relying on the narrative that had been pushed onto them for generations—where "crazy" is the norm associated with mental illness.

We need to spin that narrative on its head.

Since I was in high school, I've been fully involved in the world of mental health advocacy. I worked with my county's NAMI (National Alliance on Mental Illness), even establishing a NAMI on Campus chapter at my high school. Through my work in NAMI, I not only became connected with numerous individuals with mental illness, hearing their stories and struggles, but I became intimately acquainted with the cultural stigma rampant in the Asian American community. Our efforts, from mental health awareness weeks to hosting guest speakers, were often met with awkward smiles and hesitation. Some community members were critical of our chapter's initiatives, while others pretended our club didn't even exist. And the reason for all of this? Generations of misinformation that painted mental health and mental illness as something taboo, something bad, something that should not be talked about.

As a member of the AAPI community myself, I could clearly see that my local and cultural community was holding on to outdated beliefs about mental health. While my efforts in high school helped to mitigate some of this at the school level, as seen with the increasing number of student organizations and efforts to dispel the mental health stigma, most community members were still left unaware of the truth of mental health and mental illness. As a result, my loved ones continued to struggle with their mental health, afraid to seek help due to the cultural stigmatization.

I couldn't, can't, and won't stand by that.

In order to bridge the knowledge gap, to break that toxic stigmatizing cycle, and to demystify and destigmatize mental health, stories need to be shared. This book provides those stories, compiling the experiences (and uplifting the voices) of Asian Americans across the nation who are navigating the world of mental health and mental illness. Divided into four parts, I orchestrated this book to follow the mental health journey arc. Each story, while unique, possesses a strong emphasis on one component of the journey. From the initial realization of the mental health struggle to the final step of utilizing professional services, it's a journey that promotes a new cycle: a cycle of mental well-being. At the end of each story, the key takeaway(s) will be summarized in a section called "The Breakthrough Box," to help you easily identify the lessons of, and the truths in, their experiences.

Through their stories, we can instill the empathy that the Asian American community is missing, while helping those of us outside of the API community understand the values and barriers that make it difficult for API folks to seek help. By providing expert opinions and the most current research, we can educate ourselves and our communities about the realities of mental health. In sharing the lessons these individuals have learned along the way, those of us struggling with our mental health can start feeling connected and gain some tools for our own journeys.

Ultimately, this book is a collection of real-life stories that serve to move us from *assuming* to *understanding*—from having it be "their" problem to deal with to a collective "ours" to resolve. It acts as a portal, transporting us across the country—from my home state of California to the eastern shores of New York—to get glimpses into the lives of ordinary people, young and old, all of whom have a story to tell. The factual information embedded in each chapter provides further context to dispel the rumors and myths, but the heart of this book lies in the stories.

We need to inform to create empathy, in order to stop the stigma. So, I implore you to listen—listen and read. Understand their journeys, discover the lessons they learned, develop that empathy. Find pieces of yourself in it, seek refuge in these shared experiences, and know that you are not alone.

Mental health isn't something we should be afraid of or avoid, nor is mental illness something to be ashamed of or hidden. It's simply a part of us (albeit, a very important part) and we need to start treating it as such.

HOW WE
GOT HERE

What is mental health?
What is considered a mental illness?
Where did the cultural stigma come from?
Is it even real?
Why are we only talking about the API community?

•••

All of these questions are valid, and before we can embark on this mental health journey of ours, they need to be answered. After all, in order to truly understand the stories of others, we need context. It is important to remove the assumptions we may hold and insert the facts. We must dispel the myths of the past and understand the truths of the present.

Our definitions for mental health are often missing key aspects; they need to be redefined. As you'll find out in this section, mental health does not solely relate to emotional wellness—it also includes psychological well-being, mindset, and mental illness.

Considering that this book focuses on the API population, it is necessary to gather knowledge not only about mental health and illness, but also on the values that define many Asian cultures. Their truths become meaningless without knowing how we got to this point—a place where the broader Asian community doesn't regard mental illness as a legitimate issue; a place where individuals struggling with their mental health are shamed and isolated; a place where we refuse to seek care in fear of others finding out.

In gaining more of an understanding about mental health, mental illness, and its relation to the AAPI community, we can better appreciate the stories shared. We'll also be able to better educate ourselves and those around us in order to facilitate greater empathy and compassion.

That's the true purpose of this section. Before we can go to "Part 1" of the mental health journey, we must first build a strong foundation.

So, let's begin.

CHAPTER 1

A BRIEF BACKGROUND
ON MENTAL HEALTH

———

Dramatic music plays in the background, the notes rising to a crescendo. The house is dark, the only source of light being the brief flashes of lightning from outside. A male figure creeps into the house, his eyes wide and crazed as his mouth turns up into a quirky twisted grin. Remnants of rain drip down his neck and clothes, leaving puddles all over the floor. His fingers are raw and bleeding lightly, a consequence of one too many nights alone with his thoughts. He holds a knife in his palm, whispering broken sentences arranged in a nonsensical pattern to something no one else in the room can see. He's breathing haphazardly, in the midst of a mental breakdown. This man is determined to kill tonight, hoping that in doing so, the voices in his head will finally quiet down. He spots his victim. It's time.

Does this scene remind you of Hollywood? From *Psycho* to *The Shining* to *Halloween*, the character archetype described above is often referenced as the classic depiction of mental illness: unpredictable, dangerous, and "psychopathic"

(Mancine, 2020). But like these movies, that portrayal is a work of fiction. The reality is usually far less extreme. Unsurprisingly, however, with popular media showcasing mental health in this way, there remains a continued misunderstanding about what mental health is, what it includes, and what it can look like.

LET'S REDEFINE MENTAL HEALTH AND MENTAL ILLNESS

Our general understanding tends to vacillate between two extremes: "good" mental health and "bad" mental health. Many of us believe having "good" mental health means being in a state of continued happiness, while "bad" mental health is a declaration of mental insanity. In reality, however, neither is correct.

According to the Oxford University Press's *Lexico.com* (2021), mental health is defined as a "person's condition with regard to their psychological and emotional well-being." In this way, mental health relates to everyone, whether or not one experiences mental illness. Feeling stressed or overwhelmed? That relates to your mental health. Feeling sad or hopeless? That's also part of mental health. Feeling joyous? Still mental health.

As the Mayo Clinic Staff (2019b) describes, the state of your mental health is determined by the overall wellness of how you think, regulate your feelings, and behave. Your daily emotions, how you react to various situations—that all relates to your mental health. An individual experiencing "good" mental health is able to "express and deal with both positive and *negative* emotions," initiate and "maintain good relationships with others," carry out various responsibilities, and cope with stressful situations (Mental Health

Foundation, 2021). In our lifetime, many of us will most certainly shift between periods of good and poor mental health. That's why, much like our physical health, it is vital we take care of our mental health, too.

If we aren't proactive about caring for it, it can have unintended negative repercussions on nearly every aspect of our lives, from our relationships to our careers. Persistent poor mental health can decrease our productivity, limit our ability to cultivate fulfilling relationships, and worsen our overall quality of life. It can even affect our physical health, manifesting as a whole host of physical issues, from gastrointestinal problems (associated with anxiousness) to migraines (from persistent low mood) to uveitis (an inflammatory eye disease that can cause temporary blindness, sometimes seen in those with untreated bipolar disorder) (Pattani, 2019). Thus, it is important to ensure we have proper outlets to deal with our emotions, like exercise, meditation, journaling, or talking with a trusted individual (for example, a friend or a therapist). It's essential to manage our feelings and thoughts so that they don't interfere with our daily activities. This is all part of mental wellness, after all.

However, when our emotions or thoughts *do* interfere with our daily lives and tasks or cause us distress, it is considered a mental health disorder. It doesn't mean that having the occasional bad day, feeling immense sadness or elation over a particular situation, or being fearful of certain things automatically equates to a mental health disorder or mental illness. It's only when these feelings *constantly* prevent us from moving through our day is it considered a disorder (Mayo Clinic Staff, 2019d). (It is important to note, though, that this definition is starting to become outdated. There is an increasing amount of research that shows individuals with mental health disorders can also be high-functioning—something that will be discussed in Chapter 10).

For instance, does your fear of social situations prevent you from stepping a foot outside of your house? Do your feelings of sadness never leave, making it impossible to get out of bed most days? Do you feel an uncontrollable feeling of elation and energy that leads to days of impulsive spending? These are just some examples of how our emotions, thoughts, feelings, and behaviors interfere with our ability to function for an extended period of time. It may become harder to maintain personal or family relationships, difficult to participate in social settings and important activities, perform at work or school, or even learn (Mayo Clinic Staff, 2019b).

In these situations, we may need to seek outside resources to help us manage our emotional and mental state in order to do what we truly want to do. However, that is always easier said than done. While there are a growing number of resources and efforts to help those with a mental illness, there is still a worldwide stigma associated with accessing and using these resources.

This stigma didn't materialize out of nowhere, however. Rather, it is a result of a decades-long misunderstanding of mental health and mistreatment of those with mental illness.

TRACING THE MENTAL HEALTH STIGMA THROUGH HISTORY

While the concept of *mental health* in regard to the general population is a fairly recent development, there is an extensive history of how the world (including the United States) has regarded those with mental illness. For much of history, those with mental illness or any associated mental health disorders were considered "abnormal." However, what was deemed as "abnormal behavior" varied from culture to culture and time period to time period; it was all dependent on the sociocultural norms of the region. Thus, any individual that greatly deviated from the region's cultural expectations (whether or not they fit with our modern definition of "mental illness") was deemed "mentally sick," often isolated from the rest of society or silenced. For example, in many Southeast Asian cultures (pre-colonization), gender was traditionally viewed as something fluid (Peletz, 2006); trans folks and crossdressers were a norm, not viewed as "other" or "abnormal." But in Britain and other European countries, where gender was seen as strictly binary, those who were trans or who cross-dressed were often viewed as mentally ill people who needed psychiatric intervention (Carr and Spandler, 2019).

Now, the reasoning behind and explanations for such "behavioral deviations" also varied from culture to culture. In some, such as those where Christianity or Catholicism and their ideals were dominant (like in colonial Philippines during the sixteenth to the nineteenth century and Samoa until the 1960s), mental illness was thought of as a result of demonic possession—in other words, supernatural causes (Samaniego, 2017). Regions with great Islamic influence attributed mental illness and poor mental health to an imbalance of the body and soul, when material or spiritual needs weren't fulfilled (Minas and Lewis, 2017). Chinese medicine believed that an imbalance between *yin* and *yang* (the complementary bodily forces)—due to a non-harmonious life— was the cause (Tseng, 1973). Other cultures, like the Hindus of India, suspected there were multiple causes, from demonic possession to the wrong diet (Abhyankar, 2015); to them, most cases of mental illness had both spiritual and physical origins (Queensland Health, 2011). In regions not as heavily influenced by Christianity, Islam, or Judaism, it was believed to have been due to inconsistencies and/or abnormalities in the physical body (somatogenic causes) (Miller, n.d.).

Depending on the believed cause of the perceived abnormality, individuals would receive different treatments. During prehistoric times (around 6500 BCE), holes were drilled into the skulls of those with mental illness, in order to "release" the evil spirits that were trapped inside. In India, treatment addressed both the spiritual and physical aspects, consisting of the recitation of religious *mantras*, ancient Indian breathing techniques, and a change in diet (Kang, 2010). In the Philippines, treatment usually consisted of an exorcism by the church or the use of physical and psychological distress by *herbolarios* (folk healers) to chase off the mental illness (Samaniego, 2017). Chinese medicine focused on using "talking cures" (i.e., talking about their feelings and thoughts) and emotional manipulation (inciting a certain emotion to counteract the "irregular emotional state") as treatment, along with resolving the mentally ill individual's tangible sources of distress (Chiang, 2014). Places that looked to somatogenic causes would use strong-smelling substances or surgical techniques on the body to "fix" the identified abnormality (Andrews, 2018).

Regardless of the cause and treatment, mental health disorders—or any other deviations from the norm—were seen in a negative light. They were something individuals had to be "saved" from; they were an indicator of a sinful person, a testament to their immorality, evidence of their inability to lead a balanced life. But around 400 BCE, we started seeing a shift in the perception of mental illness (PBS, n.d.).

Greek physician Hippocrates was one of the first recorded to reject any supernatural causes, instead looking toward psychogenic ones (in which traumatic or stressful experiences cause maladaptive behaviors, thoughts, or perceptions). As a result, Hippocrates and many other Greek physicians (like Galen) would treat mental illness by changing their environment, switching their occupation, or encouraging household support. In addition to this, an imbalance in one of the four essential bodily fluids (blood, yellow bile, black bile, and phlegm) was also believed to be a possible cause among Greek physicians; the resulting treatment was medication or the administration of medicinal techniques like bloodletting. Generally, these somatic sources, rather than psychogenic ones, were more commonly accepted as the source of mental health issues among various cultures, especially in many Asian and Pacific Islander countries. Thus, most regions focused on "balancing" the bodies of their mentally ill patients (Miller, n.d.).

Interestingly, during this time period where Greek thought and philosophy prevailed, mental illness wasn't regarded as negative or shameful. Rather, due to the psychogenic school of thought, it was viewed as something beyond the control of—and not the fault of—the mentally ill individual. However, by the eleventh century, as a result of the increasing influence of religion, the more traditional supernatural beliefs regarding mental illness started returning to Europe—and, following extensive colonization campaigns, to various parts of Asia and the Pacific Islands. Exorcisms, religious conversion, detainment, isolation, and persecution became the norm, reinstating the negative attitudes of earlier centuries (Zilboorg and Henry, 1941).

This viewpoint even spread to the United States, persisting as the country headed into the nineteenth century. Regarded as "undesirable" and "dangerous," those with mental illness were forcibly separated from the general public and placed in state-sanctioned asylums. The asylums were rife with abuse and torture, as residents were chained to walls and surrounded by filth. Belief in the somatogenic theory (imbalance in the body caused mental insanity) led to the use of bloodletting, tranquilizer chairs, gyrators, mercury, and hot/cold baths as treatment. While horrific, this subhuman treatment was a result of a general belief that the mentally ill did not have the capability to control themselves or understand reason, that they (mentally) were nothing more than animals (Miller, n.d.).

Though the negative stigmatization of mental illness was still widespread, in the nineteenth century, activist Dorothea Dix (a retired schoolteacher) started lobbying for better living conditions after visiting some of these asylums. Decades later, through the tireless efforts of Dix and other activists, state hospitals were established, complete with more formalized psychiatric care from medical professionals and staff (PBS, n.d.). But as veterans (many of whom were suffering from PTSD) returned from war and families struggled to care for their mentally ill relatives, these institutions started becoming overcrowded, underfunded, and understaffed (Novella, 2010). By the 1950s, these mental hospitals were drawing criticism for their poor conditions and human rights violations, resulting in the birth of the deinstitutionalization movement, which sought to end asylum-based health care. Coupled with developments in antipsychotic drugs, psychotherapy, and psychiatry, activists wanted to see the end of in-patient hospitals and the start of outpatient treatment (PBS, 2021).

As a result of this movement's efforts, the Community Mental Health Centers Act of 1963 was enacted, which closed the vast majority of state psychiatric hospitals (PBS, n.d.). Only individuals who posed an imminent danger to themselves or others were admitted to the few remaining psychiatric hospital facilities. In other words, the majority of those with mental health issues were left to their own devices, with few resources or programs to assist them (Novella, 2010). Without much government assistance, community support (due to decades of the stigmatization of mental illness), affordable housing, or funding for outpatient treatment, the incarceration rate among those with mental illness started climbing (Prins, 2011). Consequently, the general public started to *further* associate crime and other negative perceptions with the mentally ill, leading to a general stigma around mental health (and, subsequently, a stigma around needing and accessing these resources) (Unite for Sight, 2021). During this time, the United States (and the world) came to view mental health as the "schizophrenic who was going to come and stab you." Mental illness was seen in the extreme, with little empathy or understanding for those afflicted with these invisible illnesses. Danger and instability became associated with mental illness.

Today, these stigmatizations are still quite pervasive. But in the past two decades, there has been a significant push to promote a true understanding of mental health and mental illness, in order to encourage more individuals to seek treatment while eradicating the judgment toward those with mental health disorders. From our schools and workplaces taking on a more pro-mental-health approach to an increasing availability of professional mental health services, the twenty-first century has been seeing vast improvements in how those with mental illness are regarded. We're finally starting to recognize that mental health and mental illness are, like many things, a spectrum. They manifest in a whole host of ways, affecting various people differently. Treatment has also become more holistic, with different schools of thought (psychotherapy, behavioral therapy, somatic, etc.) being used to help individuals better manage their mental health.

However, there is still a long way to go, especially as various communities struggle to accept those with mental illnesses and individuals feel ashamed or afraid to seek help. In recognizing the long history of stigma we harbor as a nation (which affects the way many racial and ethnic groups perceive mental health today), we can move forward in eradicating its effects in our country. Nonetheless, our knowledge about mental illness and its causes has grown through the centuries, which has allowed us to improve the way we treat and regard mental health and mental illness.

WHAT CAUSES MENTAL HEALTH DISORDERS?

Historically, we've looked to the supernatural and imbalanced body systems as the source of mental illness. But in the past couple of decades, we've come to understand that is not necessarily the case.

While the cause of a mental health disorder can vary between individuals, there are three main ones according to the Mayo Clinic: genetics, environment, and brain chemistry. For genetics, mental health and mental illness tend to be more common in those whose blood relatives also have a history of mental health issues. Additionally, certain genes increase your risk of developing a mental health disorder—but it doesn't necessarily mean one will develop a mental health issue just by having a genetic predisposition for it. (We'll see why in a second). As for the environmental cause, it refers to both pre- and post-birth conditions. Pre-birth environmental causes can include exposure to alcohol or drugs, toxins, and stressors while in the womb (Mayo Clinic Staff, 2019d). Post-birth exposures are comprised of various forms of trauma (such as abuse, neglect, social isolation, discrimination, military combat), stressful situations (like unemployment, homelessness, poverty, being a long-term caregiver for someone), physical injuries or chronic illnesses, and loss (Mind Infoline, 2017). With brain chemistry causes, the neural networks for neurotransmitters (naturally occurring brain chemicals that carry signals between your brain and body) are impaired or changed; usually, such a cause is linked with mood disorders (Mayo Clinic Staff, 2019d).

None of these factors are mutually exclusive; in fact, most individuals with a mental health issue can trace it back to a combination of these causes. For example, genes *and* a certain environment/situation can lead to the development of a mental health disorder. More specifically, for example, if an individual with chromosome 3p25-26 (the "depression gene") is faced with job loss and doesn't have a strong support system, they'll be more likely (note: not guaranteed) to develop depression (Faris, 2021). But without that specific situation (job loss and no support), there isn't a "trigger" for that gene to potentially be expressed.

Ultimately, these three factors (genetics, environment, and brain chemistry) are the main root sources of mental health disorders. While it is important to understand the underlying factors and causes that can lead to the development of mental illnesses, they are of little consequence to medical professionals when providing a diagnosis. Instead, psychiatrists focus on identifying the specific *type* of mental illness an individual has, as that allows medical providers to deliver a targeted and effective treatment plan.

But what are these "types," you may ask? Well, we merely need to look to the American Psychiatric Association for answers.

DIVING INTO THE DSM

Consolidated by the American Psychiatric Association, the DSM (which stands for *Diagnostic and Statistical Manual of Mental Disorders*) has been the premier publication used by medical professionals when diagnosing a patient in the United States (American Psychiatric Association, 2021). (*Side note:* you might have also heard of the ICD-10-CM. The ICD-10-CM (International Classification of Diseases, 10th Edition, Clinical Modification) is also a tool used by mental health professionals, but more so to codify the diagnosis for insurance purposes (Foley, 2016)). In the latest edition (the DSM-V), there are approximately three hundred different mental health disorders listed (American Psychiatric Association, 2021). These disorders can be divided into nineteen main categories, organized by their shared characteristics (i.e., by cause, symptom, psychological or physiological effects, etc.).

For reference, below is a brief overview of the nineteen categories. For more information about what these disorders constitute and how they are experienced, I recommend visiting some of the websites included at the end of this book (under the chapter/section titled "Resources for Further Exploration").

- Neurodevelopmental Disorders: These disorders refer to disabilities that are mainly associated with the neurological system and brain (Cherry, 2020).
  - Includes intellectual disabilities, communication disorders, autism spectrum disorders, attention-deficit/hyperactivity disorders, specific learning disorders, and motor disorders (American Psychiatric Association, 2013).
- Schizophrenia Spectrum and Other Psychotic Disorders: These disorders are chronic psychiatric conditions that affect an individual's thoughts, emotions, and behavior, often accompanied by hallucinations, delusions, etc. (Cherry, 2020).
  - Includes catatonia and other schizophrenic/schizoaffective disorders (American Psychiatric Association, 2013).
- Bipolar and Related Disorders: This class of disorders is characterized by shifts in mood, as well as changes in activity and energy levels; it is usually marked by a shift between periods of elation and depression (Cherry, 2020).
  - Includes cyclothymic and bipolar disorders (American Psychiatric Association, 2013).
- Depressive Disorders: These disorders are a type of mood disorder that is characterized by the presence of sad, hopeless, or irritable moods. They often include physical and/or cognitive symptoms and can vary widely in their duration and severity (Cherry, 2020).
  - Includes disruptive mood dysregulation disorders, major depressive disorder, and premenstrual dysphoric disorder (American Psychiatric Association, 2013).

- Anxiety Disorders: This class is characterized by excessive (and persistent) fear, worry, anxiousness, nervousness, or other related behavioral disturbances. They are essentially an emotional response to a threat or future threat (whether or not that threat is real and/or perceived) (Cherry, 2020).
  - Includes specific phobias, social anxiety disorders, and panic disorders (American Psychiatric Association, 2013).
- Obsessive-Compulsive and Related Disorders: They are characterized by obsessive or compulsive behaviors, often interfering with daily activities (Cherry, 2020).
  - Includes hoarding disorder, trichotillomania, and excoriation disorder (American Psychiatric Association, 2013).
- Trauma- and Stressor-Related Disorders: These disorders are characterized by previous exposure to a stressful or traumatic event. They lead to symptoms quite similar to anxiety disorders, but the cause is different than anxiety disorders (Cherry, 2020).
  - Include reactive attachment disorder, acute stress disorder, and disinhibited social engagement disorder (American Psychiatric Association, 2013).
- Dissociative Disorders: These are psychological disorders that are characterized by a *dissociation* (disruption) in consciousness, identity, and/or memory (Cherry, 2020).
  - Includes dissociative amnesia, depersonalization/derealization disorder, and dissociative identity disorder (American Psychiatric Association, 2013).
- Somatic Symptom and Related Disorders: This class of disorders is characterized by physical symptoms that don't have a diagnosable physical cause (Cherry, 2020).

- Includes illness anxiety disorder, conversion disorder, and factitious disorder (American Psychiatric Association, 2013).

- Feeding and Eating Disorders: These disorders are usually characterized by an obsessive preoccupation with weight, leading to disruptive eating patterns that negatively affect physical and mental health (Cherry, 2020).
  - Includes pica disorder, rumination disorder, and avoidant/restrictive food intake disorder (American Psychiatric Association, 2013).

- Elimination Disorders: This class is characterized by the inappropriate elimination of urine or feces. These disorders are usually diagnosed in childhood or early adolescence (American Psychiatric Association, 2014).
  - Includes enuresis disorder and encopresis disorder (American Psychiatric Association, 2013).

- Sleep-Wake Disorders: These are characterized by interruptions in sleep patterns, which often lead to distress and impaired daytime functioning (Cherry, 2020).
  - Includes breathing-related sleep disorders and parasomnias (American Psychiatric Association, 2013).

- Sexual Dysfunctions: This class refers to disorders where there is a persistent and recurrent issue with one's sexual response, desire, orgasm, or pain, which can often cause distress to oneself or one's partner (Mayo Clinic Staff, 2020).
  - Includes delayed ejaculation and female orgasmic disorder (American Psychiatric Association, 2013).

- Gender Dysphoria Disorder: This disorder is characterized by feelings of distress and/or discomfort due to possessing a gender identity that differs from one's

sex-related physical characteristics (or sex assigned at birth) (Mayo Clinic Staff, 2019a).
  - Includes gender dysphoria (American Psychiatric Association, 2013).
- Disruptive, Impulse Control, and Conduct Disorders: These disorders involve an inability to control emotions or behaviors, which can often lead to harm (to others or even oneself) (Casarella, 2021).
  - Includes antisocial personality disorder, kleptomania, and oppositional defiant disorder (American Psychiatric Association, 2013).
- Substance-Related and Addictive Disorders: These disorders are characterized by the use of and abuse of different substances (Cherry, 2020).
  - Includes alcohol-related disorders, caffeine-related disorders, cannabis-related disorders, hallucinogen-related disorders, inhalant-related disorders, opioid-related disorders, sedative/hypnotic/anxiolytic-related disorders, stimulant-related disorders, and tobacco-related disorders (American Psychiatric Association, 2013).
- Neurocognitive Disorders: This class of disorders is characterized by deficits in cognitive function that were not present at birth or early life (Cherry, 2020).
  - Includes delirium and major or mild neurocognitive disorders (American Psychiatric Association, 2013).
- Personality Disorders: These are characterized by patterns of maladaptive thoughts, feelings and/or behaviors, which can usually lead to serious harmful or negative effects on relationships and other aspects of life (Casarella, 2021).

- Includes general personality disorder, paranoid personality disorder, histrionic personality disorder, Cluster A Personality Disorders, Cluster B Personality Disorders, Cluster C Personality Disorders, and avoidant personality disorder (American Psychiatric Association, 2013).

- Paraphilic Disorders: These are characterized by recurrent, intense, and sexually arousing behaviors and/or urges that can potentially cause harm to others or oneself (Brown, 2021).
  - Includes voyeuristic disorder, frotteuristic disorder, and transvestic disorder (American Psychiatric Association, 2013).

- Other Mental Disorders: The mental health disorders in this category do not quite fall into any of the other above categories. Those diagnosed with a mental health issue from this category are usually a result of obvious emotional/mental distress, but without enough of a "match" to the other specified disorders.
  - Includes other specified mental disorders due to another medical condition (American Psychiatric Association, 2013).

Referencing the illnesses outlined above from the DSM-V, the psychiatrist "matches" the patient to the relevant diagnosis based on the symptoms reported, the results of diagnostic tests (like PHQ-2 and PHQ-9 (American Psychological Association, 2020)), and the psychiatrist's own observations (Mayo Clinic Staff, 2019c). The severity of the mental health disorder depends on the symptoms, frequency of associated behaviors, and level of distress or danger it causes the individual. In this way, psychiatrists are able to diagnose and treat patients in a more precise manner.

•••

Ultimately, the world of mental health is clearly vast and untapped. The information touched on in this chapter only serves as surface-level information, to provide background and context that will allow you, the readers, to better appreciate the stories shared in this book. More than that, it is to equip everyone, no matter how little one may know, with an understanding of mental health and mental illness. Only by understanding can we move past judgment in our communities—including the Asian American community.

CHAPTER 2

ASIAN AMERICANS AND MENTAL HEALTH

———

Mental health and mental illness don't discriminate. They affect *everyone*, regardless of color, religion, culture, or creed. So, why are we only focusing on the AAPI community?

While it is true that mental health is universal, the way it is viewed and understood tends to vary between different (racial) groups of people. Mental health in the Asian/Pacific Islander community is regarded quite differently compared to the white community or the Black community. The factors, situations, and histories—all of which impact how mental health is experienced for a racial group—vary. Thus, it would be an injustice to try and capture every group's experience within one book. If we did, we wouldn't be able to fully appreciate and understand the stories shared. That's why, as a South Asian woman myself, I decided to speak on the racial group *my* background comes from.

The Asian American community has suffered in silence for a long time. Its members haven't had a chance to truly share their stories with the cultural community—or beyond.

This book serves as a place to amplify their mental health experiences, both within the context of their identity and as individuals living in the United States. Therefore, before we can dive into the stories of this book, it is important to glean a basic understanding of the values, history, and perspectives of the Asian American and Pacific Islander community.

ACKNOWLEDGING THE DIVERSITY OF ASIAN AMERICANS AND PACIFIC ISLANDERS

Regarded as the fastest-growing group in the United States, the Asian American and Pacific Islander (AAPI) population is one of the most ethnically diverse racial groups in the nation. Making up 6.1 percent of the United States population, the term AAPI (or API, Asian/Pacific Islander) refers to individuals with cultural or ethnic backgrounds from Asia or the Pacific Islands (U.S. Department of Health and Human Services (OMH), 2021b; OMH, 2021a). These individuals can be loosely divided into five different regional/ethnic identities: Central Asians, East Asians, Native Hawaiians/Pacific Islanders, Southeast Asians, and South Asians (Asian Pacific Institute on Gender-Based Violence, 2021). (Note: those with backgrounds from West Asia—Iran, Iraq, Saudi Arabia, etc.— generally do not identify with or use the term "Asian American/Pacific Islander." Rather, they tend to identify with and are referred to as part of the Southwest Asian and North African (SWANA) community, which leaves them out of this definition. Even among the studies conducted and reports written on AAPI populations, those from West/Southwest Asia are usually excluded from the definition.)

Of course, with Asia and the Pacific Islands consisting of over forty individual countries, there are countless ethnicities contained within each of these regions. From the Afghani and Mongolian people of Central Asia to the Korean and Tai-wanese people of East Asia to the Fijian and Samoan people of the Pacific Islands to the Cambodian and Filipino people of Southeast Asia to the Bangladeshi and Nepali people of South Asia, each of these individual ethnic groups holds its own unique practices, languages, and histories (Asian Pacific Institute on Gender-Based Violence, 2021). Even though religiously, Islam, Hinduism, Catholicism/Christianity, and Buddhism dominate, regional variations in the deities and rituals exist (Pew Forum, 2012). The languages spoken, the myths written, the traditions followed—they all vary.

Even just *within* the Asian Indian community (individuals with a background from India), there are over twenty-eight nationally recognized cultures and over one hundred languages spoken (PTI, 2018). Similarly, other Asian communities and countries also have their own variations within the cultural/ethnic group. To go into the specific languages, practices, and history of each would be far too complex—it would take a whole book just to do that! In this way, the term "Asian American" is a gross generalization that fails to portray the cultural diversity found in these racial groups. In fact, it wasn't until 2000 that "Pacific Islander" and "Asian" were considered two separate racial groups in the US Census (Yamada et al., 2021). (However, for the sake of clarity in my writing, I will be using "Asian," "Asian American," "API," and "AAPI" interchangeably to reference the Asian American and Pacific Islander populations my book is focused on. The reason why is explained in my "Author's Note" section at the beginning of the book.) That's why I recommend you take a quick read into the cultural backgrounds of the individuals featured in this book, as you come across them; doing so will only expand your knowledge and help you develop a deeper appreciation for the diversity of Asian/Pacific Islander cultures.

Currently, as surveyed by the Pew Research Center in 2019, of the AAPI population currently residing in the United States, 23 percent are of Chinese origin, 20 percent are Indian, 18 percent are Filipino, 9 percent are Vietnamese, 8 percent are Korean, 6 percent are Japanese, and all other ethnicities (specifically, Pakistani, Thai, Cambodian, Hmong, Laotian, Bangladeshi, Nepalese, Burmese, Indonesian, Sri Lankan, Malaysian, Mongolian, Bhutanese, Native Hawaiian, Samoan, and Fijian) account for that last 15 percent. The Asian Americans/Pacific Islanders of this nation are varied not only in population but also by socioeconomic status. In 2019, the median annual household income for API folks was $85,800 (Budiman and Ruiz, 2021a), but when you look at the median incomes for different ethnic subgroups, there are drastic differences. Asian Indians have the highest median income at $119,000 and Filipino Americans follow close behind at $90,400. On the other end of the income spectrum, Burmese and Nepalese have the lowest median incomes, at $44,400 and $55,000 respectively (Budiman and Ruiz, 2021b).

These observed differences come from the variation in the way Asian Americans have immigrated to the United States. There is an unfortunate "model minority" myth that paints Asian Americans as "well-to-do" individuals coming from privileged backgrounds. While that is most definitely true for some families and (generalized) ethnic groups, the reality is that the United States has a long, rich, and varied history in regard to Asian immigration. For example, Asian Indians and Asian Koreans mainly came to the United States as high-skilled professionals (Pew Forum, 2013); in contrast, those from Cambodia, Laos, and Vietnam came to the United States mostly as refugees (Constante, 2020). The former group came into the United States with economic support, while the latter group came here with little to their name and almost no support system. These circumstantial differences have had a drastic impact on these two groups' socioeconomic statuses and outcomes. It is similar for the other ethnic groups that fall under the term "Asian American and Pacific Islander," where certain groups have been actively discriminated against for centuries via policy, while others were only allowed in if they were wealthy and/or possessed a skill needed by the nation (Kiang, n.d.). But despite all of these differences, there *are* some shared values among this expansive racial group.

FROM THE NORTH TO THE SOUTH: THE VALUES THAT UNITE API FOLKS ACROSS THE WORLD

Though they come from different backgrounds and have different traditions, there are four values that act as the common thread that connects the various API ethnic groups together: work, family responsibility, community development, and investment in education. Often stemming from the shared immigrant experience, whether fifth generation or first, API families that come to the United States usually model their lives with these values in mind. In contrast to the Western principles of individualism, Asia and the Pacific Islands place a distinct emphasis on the *collective* (Xie, 2018).

In China, Japan, and Korea, there is a popular saying: *the nail that sticks out gets hammered down* (Xie, 2018). Even among the Samoans, a "collectivist system of governance," *fa'amatai*, is emphasized, in which community members are expected to put the "best interests of the community and family members above their own" (Hansen, 2020). From a young age, it is taught that conformity, social harmony, and deference to authority outweigh individual uniqueness, needs, and desires. For the vast majority of Asian Americans and Pacific Islanders, the dominant cultural practices and ideologies stress the need to place others, *especially* the family and the community, before oneself (Xie, 2018). If you do or experience something that deviates from the norm, it isn't only you who is shamed; the entire family and/or community also experiences that shame. Even in the decision-making process, it is often seen as selfish if you choose to do something without regard to the family.

As such, one's actions are no longer one's own. Rather, they are a reflection of one's community, lineage, or family; they are tied to the greater whole. Thus, individuals find themselves experiencing this often-underlying pressure to present themselves to their family and the larger cultural community in a way that communicates normalcy. Consequently, this "pressure," created from the collectivist cultures of Asian Americans, plays a key role in the way mental health and mental illness are regarded. More specifically, for many families, mental illness is seen as something shameful, a weakness that should be hidden away from the public (Tanap, 2019). Due to the existing negative stereotypes and viewpoints about mental illness, if it gets out that a family member has a mental health disorder, it will only reflect harshly on the family as a whole. People would attribute the diagnosis to a shortcoming of the family—perhaps, a result of poor parenting, too much freedom and privilege, or an unstable childhood. Therefore, to avoid that, families attempt to hide such things, sometimes even denying the reality that their child, or that they themselves, have a mental illness. They avoid seeking professional medical help, instead (understandably, because this is what the collective preaches and teaches) clinging to traditional concepts that a "stronger mind" or religion can eradicate the symptoms of the mental illness (Tanap, 2019).

As for mental health in general (i.e., taking care of your emotional and mental well-being), that isn't even a concept in many Asian cultures. Feelings, emotions, mental anguish—they are all considered as part of life, something that must be endured silently and without complaint.

This stigmatization of mental illness and ideal of silent endurance didn't appear out of nowhere, however. It is true that there is a lack of understanding currently around mental health and illness, but there are also multiple theories on *how* this stigma and practice of hiding the mentally ill even came to be. One such theory is the *survival theory*.

IMMIGRATION AND ASSIMILATION: THEORIES ON HOW THE AAPI MENTAL HEALTH STIGMA CAME TO BE
As described by Dr. Anjabeen Ashraf in an Instagram post, Asians and Pacific Islanders, like other minority groups, have experienced institutional racism and oppression throughout the decades (@dranjabeenashraf, July 29, 2020). From the early arrivals of Chinese immigrants during the 1850s (History Detectives, 2014) to the political refugees from Vietnam to the more recent uptick in Korean, Indian, and Pacific Islander immigration, Asian Americans have been flowing into the United States in significant numbers for more than a century. However, with their arrival came various acts and policies of prejudice, including the Chinese Exclusion Act of 1882 (which barred immigration from China) and the Immigration Act of 1917 (which barred immigration from virtually all of Asia and the Pacific Islands). Along with these policies

that kept Asian immigrants at bay, those who were already living in the United States were exploited for cheap labor (such as the Filipino, Japanese, and Korean Americans, and Native Hawaiians on the pineapple and sugar plantations located in Hawai'i during the 1900s), while enduring harassment and race-based hate crimes (Pew Forum, 2013; Odo, 2018). For example, Japanese Americans, following the attack on Pearl Harbor, were gathered into internment camps where they were forced to endure Nazi-Germany-like living conditions. Even in the modern-day, hate crimes against Asian Americans, such as toward the Sikhs and Muslim Americans following 9/11 or East Asians after the discovery of COVID-19, continue to plague society.

Thus, due to these conditions that consistently limited Asian Americans and put them in harm's way, it led to the development of a constant "survival mode." In order to survive and succeed in a nation where race affected one's treatment and opportunities, AAPI folks needed to adopt an attitude of endurance; they needed to show that they were "model citizens." Anything that may have alluded to an "imperfection" was to be silenced or hidden—that included signs of mental illness, as it was regarded as a negative aspect in dominant American society. In the effort to assimilate, the stigma already held by the AAPI community from previous European colonization was compounded by the negative "American" viewpoint on mental health. Now, instead of at least relying on the support of the larger community to deal with one's mental illness, it became the norm to endure one's struggles in silence and alone. It also became commonplace to ostracize those who showed signs of these perceived "imperfections," in fear of being associated with them due to the collectivist ideals that persisted. Slowly, in this way, the Asian American community became one gripped by (an even more) severe stigmatization of mental illness—one that exists even today.

However, this is only one of many theories.

Others ascertain that the practices of hiding in silence already existed in Asian cultures—and those practices were only brought into the United States when Asian families immigrated here. For example, in India, it wasn't (and still isn't) unusual for families to chain their mentally ill at temples, hidden away from the world and receiving what they believed to be "proper" treatment from religious priests (Sharma and Krishna, 2013). Individuals with more overt symptoms of a mental health disorder were often isolated from society by their caregivers/families, in order to protect the family status and avoid the social repercussions (like diminished marriage and career prospects) of revealing a diagnosis (Kudva et al., 2020). In many Southeast Asian countries, specifically Indonesia, the practice of *pasung* (the act of physically restraining and confining family members with mental illness) was—and continues to be—extremely common (Minas and Diatri, 2008). It was banned only relatively recently, in 1977 (Sharma, 2020). With such preexisting practices of hiding and ignoring mental health disorders, it comes as no surprise that when families come into the United States, the same viewpoints on mental illness persist. It ultimately became a practice that was passed down through the generations, reinforced by how American society treated those who were mentally ill.

Regardless of which theories are true (though, the source of the stigma is likely due to a combination of the reasons presented), it doesn't change the reality that the stigma is strong, and it is pervasive—and it is impacting our communities in ways we can never truly fathom.

LAST WORDS BEFORE WE EMBARK ON OUR MENTAL HEALTH "JOURNEY"

As it stands, second- and third-generation Asian Americans are more likely to *develop* mental health disorders. Yet, API individuals are less likely to *utilize* mental health resources—but have some of the highest rates of using emergency services due to a severe mental health crisis. In other words, the stigmatization, reluctance to seek services early, and practice of silent endurance are harming the API community.

We need to challenge that.

While it is true mental health is just another facet of life, it isn't meant to be suppressed or dealt with alone; sometimes, when we're struggling with it, we need outlets, professional help, and medicinal management—*not* silence, endurance, and isolation.

That's what these stories are here to show us.

Not only are mental health and mental illness a part of life that we need to accept, but we also have to allow ourselves to be open to the possibility of using outside help and resources. There is no shame in having a mental illness or struggling with our mental health; we are not failures for relying on others to achieve mental wellness.

Empathy and understanding are the keys here. Whether it's for ourselves or for others, these keys are necessary if we want to revolutionize the Asian American and Pacific Islander community (and beyond) into one that wholly accepts those with a mental illness, supports them in their mental health journeys, and encourages them to seek help. So, as we head into the heart of this book, keep the Asian histories and values discussed in this chapter in mind. In doing so, we will better understand their stories and better appreciate *why* these stories are being shared in the first place.

PART 1

CONTENDING WITH REALITY

The mental health journey starts with a realization—a self-awareness of one's mental state. Sometimes it is sudden, hitting us at our lowest points and least expected moments. Other times, it is gradual—a culmination of events over the past couple of months or years. But it is always a profound understanding that *we are struggling.* That struggle is found in many forms. It's the thoughts that creep into the forefront of our minds, creating a sense of panic and anxiety at every turn; it's the feeling that we're slipping further and further from reality; it's the slow disinterest in our world, then our homes, then in ourselves—until we're nothing but a hollow shell.

No matter where or when or how, that self-awareness remains one of the most important steps of any mental health journey. It is, after all, the step that kick-starts our drive to seek help. It's the step that gives us permission to heal and recover.

For Sara Ahmed and James, it was the step that changed the course of their lives.

Though they come from different walks of life (one a middle-aged mother, the other a college student), Ahmed and James share a similar start to their mental health journeys. Neither was open to professional help until they admitted to *themselves* that they needed it. And to reach that stage of self-awareness and self-acceptance? It took time.

Their stories remind us that it isn't always easy to recognize our own mental health struggles and seek help. In fact, it's pretty damn hard. However, when we *are* able to, even if it takes months or years, the payoff is unimaginable. It's the tools, resources, support, and help we gain that make it all worth it in the end.

Ultimately, Sara Ahmed and James are here to show us that awareness and acceptance are crucial to experiencing better mental health.

CHAPTER 3

SARA AHMED

———

The sun was low, starting to set on the horizon. The street—now bathed in a soft orange light—was packed with bodies, all eager to rush home. Street vendors crowded the edges of the sidewalk, the smell of their cooking—*pani puri, samosas, falafel*—filling the air. Cars drove by, honking at the vehicles in front of them and at the friendly faces passing by on the street. Women dressed in their cultural finest—*shalwar kameez, abayas, saris*—scanned the markets for the best produce at the best prices.

Further down the street, right around the corner, were rows of houses. Front doors swung open and shut as kids were called back in. Tan skin, black hair; white skin, brown hair; blue eyes, brown eyes, green too—people of different colors and ethnicities filled these homes. The neighborhood was as diverse as the cuisines served in the nearby restaurants.

Looking closer, in one of these homes was a peculiar sight: a little girl, no more than ten years of age, had her face pressed against the glass of her window. Her thick hair framed her rounded face, the black a stark contrast to the girl's pale beige skin. She was kneeling on the couch, her arms hooked across the back, waiting anxiously for her mother, who had gone out to get some groceries, to come home. It was just her older sister and her, but instead of doing homework or reading like other kids her age, she was parked by the window, wondering if her mother would ever return. Intrusive thoughts swam through her head: *What if she died? What if she never returned? What if something happened to her? Will this be the last time I ever see her?*

Suddenly, her mind quieted.

Spotting a familiar tall and wide frame amble across the front yard, the little girl released the breath she had been holding, relief evident on her face. Her mom was now home, safe and sound; there was nothing to worry about—for today, at least. Wordlessly, the girl slipped off the couch, skipping to the front door, ready to greet her mother. When the door opened, she looked up, her smile wide and adoring.

It was the same smile that greeted her newborn child, nearly twenty years later. Sara Ahmed had everything she had dreamed of. She had just given birth to her first child, surrounded by her friends, family, and loved ones. She was safe and healthy, settling down in a community-minded southern town. Her parents were home and with her; her siblings were following their passions. It seemed like everything was falling into place, finally.

So, why did she still feel so unhappy and anxious?

WELCOME TO DEVON, HOME OF IMMIGRANTS

"My story begins in the early 1980s, when I first came to the United States," Ahmed said.

Born in Pakistan, six-year-old Sara Ahmed, along with her family, had immigrated to the United States from Saudi Arabia (where her father was working as an engineer). They decided to start their brand-new American life in Chicago,

Illinois. "We moved to a small neighborhood widely known as 'Little India,'" Ahmed said. "At that time, there were four or five blocks just *filled* with brown stores."

Officially called Devon Avenue, this region of Chicago was known for its rich ethnic and cultural presence, exactly like the scene described previously. Despite being known as "Little India," Devon was home to people from all over the world—immigrants from Bangladesh, Germany, India, Pakistan, Romania, and more filled Devon's homes. The neighborhood itself—from its shops and stores to its home decors—was a blend of all these cultures. In a foreign land, this area made its residents feel a little bit more at home, as everyone bonded over their shared journeys across borders.

For Ahmed, it blessed her with an opportunity to feel not so much of an "other" in a country that was filled with those who didn't quite look like her. From her best friend, whose house was filled with the sounds of Greek, to her neighbors, who never failed to invite them over for Eid, Ahmed was surrounded by a strong sense of community. "I was blessed to not have the typical immigrant experience," Ahmed said. "I never really had a truly 'American' friend. Everyone was a first-generation immigrant like me, whose moms wore traditional clothing and spoke in their mother tongue. There was no real sense of embarrassment because that was how all of our lives were."

Although the ethnic diversity lent itself to a childhood free of shame, it also introduced, and perpetuated, many of the cultural stigmas from the homeland. One such stigma was that of mental health. In many of the countries these residents hailed from, mental health was never truly seen as legitimate and important. Rather, it was considered an over exaggeration, a reflection of one's lack of piousness, a testament to one's mental weakness. As such, it was never spoken about. "It was like it [mental health] didn't even exist," Ahmed revealed. "I don't think I remember ever—*ever*—anyone talking about it, being diagnosed with it, or suffering from it." These attitudes silenced the possibility of conversation, preventing Devon and its residents from understanding mental health.

They also ended up molding Ahmed's childhood environment into one that ignored, rather than recognized, her mental health symptoms.

FACING CHILDHOOD ANXIETY AND THE MENTAL HEALTH STIGMA

"For the most part, I had grown up as a bit of an anxious child," Ahmed said.

Her anxiousness stemmed primarily from one place: the possibility of her loved ones dying. Like in the scene described above, whenever her parents would leave the house, Ahmed's mind would be filled with uncontrollable, anxious thoughts. She would hold vigil by the window, nervously waiting for their return—or news of their sudden death.

Now, many kids do feel this sense of anxiety as they grapple with their parents' mortality, imagining scenarios in which their parents do not return home. However, there is a fine line between what is considered *typical* behavior and what is not. "When it comes to mental health," says board-certified psychiatrist Dr. Ramesh Reddy in our interview, "it's easy to believe what might just be a case of nervousness before a big speech is anxiety. In order to differentiate between a relatively 'normal' feeling and a mental health disorder, we look for evidence of a certain characteristic."

That defining characteristic being: *The behavior interferes with daily function or causes distress for the individual.* In Ahmed's case, her anxious thoughts were accompanied by an inability to complete her current task, as she would immediately station herself by the window to wait for her parents' return. Her anxiousness interrupted her ability to function while simultaneously causing her feelings of distress. In light of this, it's clear that Ahmed's actions served as evidence of that "defining characteristic," indicating a high likelihood of a mental health disorder when she was younger.

Ahmed's family, however, didn't believe these behaviors warranted a visit to the local physician. "At that point, my parents didn't have quite enough of an understanding to ever think it was a problem," Ahmed said. "It was something you found a hundred different explanations for, but not one of them was mental illness." In effect, all proposed "solutions" centered around everything but mental health or medication. Ahmed's parents would advise their daughter to pray more to alleviate those anxious thoughts. They reminded her to be grateful to God more, parroting the same advice they themselves had received growing up. To Ahmed and her family, her anxiousness wasn't a mental health issue—it was just a mind not as connected to God. As such, Ahmed didn't receive the help she needed for those anxious thoughts as a child. In fact, it was only decades later that she recognized them for what they actually were: a symptom of childhood anxiety.

Despite the lack of treatment for her unusual preoccupation with her parents' impending deaths, Ahmed had an otherwise warm and loving childhood. It was filled with positive experiences, from laughing to her heart's content around the kitchen table to trying her best friend's cultural cuisine. Ahmed, along with her two other sisters, were always encouraged to fearlessly pursue their career goals by their father. "In a time when woman empowerment wasn't really a thing," Ahmed said, "my father pushed us to be independent. Even with my mother, he made sure she knew how to drive and that she had her own car. He wanted his girls to be independent and empowered." In turn, Ahmed dove into her education, working hard to maintain near-perfect grades. Surrounded by friends who were equally studious, Ahmed would spend much of her time with her nose in a book. It was her superpower—it was where she shined. Even after her family's move to Atlanta, Georgia, the summer before high school, Ahmed kept to her brainy identity, pushing herself to do well. Midway into her high school career, Ahmed's family moved once more, this time to Minnesota. Although the winters were harsh there, it just turned into an opportunity for Ahmed to hole up inside and immerse herself in her work. "As you can see, I was a bit of a nerd," she said with a laugh.

But that "nerdy" nature brought Ahmed to the University of Houston in Houston, Texas. There, Ahmed created life-long friendships and explored her community. The longer she stayed, the more she found herself loving the city. "I knew I didn't want to leave this place *ever*," Ahmed said. And so, she never did. She continued on in her college career, ultimately teaching at her alma mater. Later on, she would enter into the field of freelance writing, publishing numerous papers, articles, and even a book—all while deepening her roots in Texas.

Now, although Ahmed was having an extremely enjoyable time in Houston, she was still experiencing the anxious thoughts of her childhood, still centered around her parents' potential deaths. However, in spite of its continued presence, Ahmed didn't consider it as anything more than just a facet of who she was: a worrier. Even with increasing conversations around mental health in the early 2000s and a greater availability of counselors and psychiatrists on college campuses (Kraft, 2011), it didn't register in Ahmed's mind that perhaps those services could be of use to her. "I believed it just didn't happen to Asians," Ahmed said. "I didn't *want* it to happen to me." So, Ahmed made her way through college, unaware and unwilling to learn about the world of mental health. She tucked away her anxious thoughts to the back of her mind, never taking a deep look at whether they were causing issues in her life. After all, she had much better things to look forward to.

One of them was her future husband. During this time of collegiate self-discovery, Ahmed met the man with whom she would end up tying the knot with. "He always made me laugh," Ahmed said, her voice soft as she spoke about her now-husband. "He was the type of man you could never get bored talking with." Their romance blossomed, leading up to marriage shortly after the pair graduated from college. A couple of years later, Ahmed gave birth to their eldest son, beginning their journey as parents. After a lifetime of working hard, achieving her goals, and reaching for success, Ahmed had everything she wanted—a budding career doing what she loved, a doting husband who supported her in all her endeavors, a gorgeous baby boy, and a forever home in family-centered Houston. It was the culmination of her life's work; it was Ahmed finally living her dreams.

Before long, however, these dreams turned into a nightmare.

THE ONSLAUGHT OF THE "BABY BLUES"

"It was after the birth of my first child, I started *really* experiencing mental health symptoms," Ahmed said. "I wanted to believe that this [my life] was so amazing, that everything was so great...but it wasn't. It was *the* most difficult time I ever had."

At thirty years old, with a newborn in hand, Ahmed had quit her job teaching at the university. After two weeks, Ahmed's husband returned to work, leaving her at home with their child. "I could not find peace of mind," Ahmed said, explaining. "I developed this obsessiveness of something happening to my son, that I would accidentally kill him while on the job, which was twenty-four/seven. It was so overwhelming." It was similar to the anxious thoughts Ahmed had all throughout her life—this time, directed toward her *son's* mortality. Similar to how it was when she was younger, Ahmed started exhibiting certain unhealthy habits. "I would constantly—and I mean, *constantly*—go and check on his breathing." Whether it was nap time or feeding time, Ahmed would hold her finger under her son's nose, checking for the gust of air that would indicate he was alive. Ahmed's mind would race with thoughts of doubt, questioning whether her actions were going to result in her child's death. It was a terrifying and anxiety-inducing state to be in.

Although Ahmed recognized her thoughts—and the accompanying behaviors—were causing her severe distress, she didn't seek help for it. "I just stayed in this mild version of depression and anxiety," Ahmed told me, "because I thought this was what happened when you became a mother. I thought you lose your identity, that it was typical to be sad and down, to not want to be part of the living. I thought we just had to stay home with the baby, doing these baby things."

It's a mindset many new mothers possess. Described as the "baby blues," the early 2000s painted these "new-mom" feelings of anxiousness, depression, and confusion as a typical response. To physicians at the time, it wasn't a cause of concern until there were thoughts of harming oneself or one's child (Smith and Segal, 2020). Even at the six-week post-birth check-up, as Ahmed recalled, the only question asked to gauge the mother's mental health was: *Are you experiencing feelings or thoughts of self-harm or harm towards your child?* In asking this sole question, it established a standard among many mothers: It wasn't a problem until you were thinking of endangering yourself or your child. The *extreme* cases became the benchmark for maternal mental health. (I must note, however, since Ahmed's time, many physicians have updated their screening, extending the questionnaire in order to catch the less extreme cases of postpartum mental health disorders. However, there is still much that can be improved in assessing maternal mental health; namely, including an extensive screening interview at *every* postpartum visit. This would increase the likelihood of detecting those with postpartum mental illness, allowing more individuals to receive help. But I digress.)

As a result, when new mothers experience mental health symptoms indicative of depression, anxiety, psychosis, or OCD, a significant proportion do not report their symptoms (Carberg and Langdon, 2021). After all, they believe them to be typical, attributing their obsessive behaviors and negative feelings to the stress of taking care of a child. In reality, as recent research has shown, these feelings should usually dissipate after two weeks (Smith and Segal, 2020). It's when it goes longer than that two-week time frame, as Dr. Ariana Witkin, a Boston-based pediatrician and maternal health consultant, explains, that the behaviors and feelings become indicative of a larger mental health issue—something many new moms don't realize or understand, even today. Thus, many of them don't receive treatment, staying in this never-ending state of suffering—Sara Ahmed included.

Throughout her first son's formative years, Ahmed struggled with her mental health and obsessive thoughts, not realizing it was a real problem. She didn't want to believe it to be anything else. "Even if someone had told me it could be a mental health issue, I wouldn't have listened to them," reflected Ahmed. "I just wanted to feel normal, so I refused to consider it as a possibility." Until then, those around Ahmed could only support, encourage, and try to provide her with healthy outlets to deal with her symptoms. For Ahmed to receive the help she needed, *she* had to be the one to come to the realization that she was struggling. It was on her to be open to the possibility of a mental health issue, to be open to help.

Five years later, she finally did.

TAKING THE FIRST STEP TOWARD MENTAL WELLNESS

"At thirty-five," Ahmed revealed, "when my second child was born, the feelings [of anxiousness and worry] intensified, lasting for months."

Having never received treatment after her first child, the birth of Ahmed's second son only compounded these feelings. Due to not seeking out help prior, her mental health symptoms got worse, increasing in severity and broadening in how they manifested. "At this point, I couldn't motivate myself to shower, to get out of the house, or look forward to things. Nothing felt exciting." When her husband announced he would take care of the kids for the night, in order for

Ahmed to spend time with her friends, she found herself wishing to stay in her room and watch television instead. "These were friends I hadn't seen in *months*, but staying home and alone sounded more enticing."

Along with the lack of motivation to do much beyond taking care of her child, Ahmed experienced uncontrollable, disruptive thoughts. "Sometimes, I would be doing something," described Ahmed, "when all of a sudden, I would start thinking about my friends. I would think about whether they replaced me, about how they were all out without me." It took her down a rabbit hole of worry, as she became further entangled in her mind. On top of that, Ahmed had frequent mood swings, as her emotions hit highs and lows, even causing uncontrollable crying at times. All of this could no longer be attributed to the stress of raising a child for the first time; after all, this was her second go at parenting.

"It was then I started asking myself whether what was happening to me was normal," Ahmed said, "because it sure didn't *feel* normal." After nearly five years of anxiousness and worry, Ahmed needed the assurance that everything was alright. Especially with the past few months presenting additional feelings of demotivation and confusion, Ahmed came to the realization that perhaps something wasn't quite right with her mental health. And so, she booked an appointment with a psychiatrist, desperate to get an answer to her question—*was there something wrong with her?*

"I went into the appointment hoping to receive news that would tell me that everything was fine," said Ahmed, "that I didn't have to obsess about [anything], that I could move on." After years of enduring an increasingly poor mental health state, Ahmed was ready for change. She was ready to get help, if that was what she needed.

After administering a couple of psychological evaluations, which included a quick questionnaire and a description of what Ahmed was experiencing, the psychiatrist prescribed Ahmed some medication. When she asked for her diagnosis, the psychiatrist expressed his reluctance to give his clients a label, but Ahmed was adamant. "I said to him, 'No, give me a label!'" Ahmed said, laughing lightly. "I wanted that diagnosis to know exactly what was wrong with me." After insisting once more, Ahmed finally received her official diagnosis: postpartum depression, or PPD for short. At first, the diagnosis confused Ahmed. *How could I be suffering from postpartum depression after three months?* Ahmed asked her doctor. The psychiatrist informed her that it wasn't uncommon—PPD could last weeks, months, even years. "It was at that moment that everything clicked," revealed Ahmed. "I realized I probably still had postpartum depression from the first baby—from which I never fully recovered from."

PPD, or postpartum depression, is a mood disorder that primarily affects women after giving birth to a baby (Centers for Disease Control and Prevention [CDC], 2020). While often left out of the conversation of mental health, its prevalence is undeniable. In a 2013 study by Dr. Katherine Wisner of Northwestern University's Feinberg School of Medicine, it was found that one in seven women experience postpartum depression. A more recent study concluded that it affects one in five (20 percent) (World Health Organization, n.d.). Both of these statistics, however, don't provide a completely accurate picture. "Postpartum depression is often underreported," says Jodie Simms-Macleod, the head of the University of Tennessee Medical Center midwifery program, in a WBIR Channel 10 article by Cole Sullivan. "It may be more common than we think." Whether in fear of having their child taken away or in fear of being labeled as an "unfit mom who overreacts," a vast majority are hesitant to seek care or report their symptoms to their physicians. Others rationalize their symptoms, believing them to be a "normal" part of motherhood, even as they span into months or years.

Although PPD can manifest in different ways, there are some common signs and symptoms that indicate its presence. These include extreme sadness or anger without warning, increased irritability, feelings of guilt or inadequacy (in being a mom), mental fogginess, trouble completing daily tasks, and a waning interest in previous hobbies. For some mothers, their PPD is accompanied by anxiety, in which the individual experiences scary, upsetting thoughts that don't go away and a heightened sense of anxiousness around the baby (or children). This anxiousness often leads to obsessive behaviors, such as repeatedly checking on the child or excessively cleaning, even at the expense of sleep or food (Mayo Clinic Staff, 2018).

While there isn't a single identified cause of PPD, there are certain reasons it can develop. For many, it is often a result of a hormonal imbalance (Mayo Clinic Staff, 2018). When pregnant, a woman's body undergoes significant physical changes, including within the brain itself. More specifically, women have a sudden significant increase in estrogen and progesterone (the two main female sex hormones) in order to optimize the uterus and the placenta for the growing child. But after giving birth, there is a dramatic drop in these two hormones (Healthline Editorial Team and Lay, 2017). This, combined with the sudden decrease of hormone production in the thyroid gland after birth, contributes to the development of postpartum depression. For others, the emotional toll of raising a child—the lack of sleep, a feeling of being overwhelmed, the struggle to find one's sense of identity—has an effect on their mental well-being, leading to an increase in depressive feelings (Mayo Clinic Staff, 2018).

Now, while PPD is quite common, it isn't universal. Those who had symptoms of anxiety or depression prior to giving birth—like Ahmed's anxious thoughts since childhood—were more likely to develop PPD (Carberg and Langdon, 2021). But many of these individuals, who come to normalize their anxiety and/or depression prior to the birth, don't seek care when they experience prolonged symptoms of anxiousness, depression, confusion, and demotivation. Instead, they fall back to their usual rationalizations, believing these experiences and feelings are simply the norm. In doing so, they don't seek out help; but without treatment (specifically, therapy, counseling, and/or medication), it never truly goes away.

It's a cycle that traps many mothers in these low feelings, sometimes causing further complications, including suicidal ideation, self-harm, harming of the baby, and psychosis. Now, for the majority, it does not get to that point. Instead, they endure a mental state that causes significant distress and endless complications in their lives. However, it would be incorrect to assume that PPD and other postpartum mental health disorders don't have serious or fatal outcomes. "In fact," Dr. Witkin shares, "deaths from suicide affect postpartum women more than hemorrhages." It's a fact that comes as a surprise to most people. Society places such a great emphasis on the physical aspects of postpartum health, it becomes easy to believe that the mental health aspects aren't as relevant.

But for women like Ahmed, that notion couldn't be more wrong. She experienced that distress and complication to a large degree—that is, until she decided to seek help.

CULTURALLY SENSITIVE TREATMENT: TRANSFORMING PATIENT OUTCOMES

"It was *such* a relief hearing my diagnosis," Ahmed told me, the sentiment evident in her tone.

Ahmed had spent the past five and a half years struggling with her mental health, not understanding what was going on in her mind. Learning that it was merely a chemical imbalance, which could be (relatively) easily addressed with medication, was a relief for Ahmed. It excited her, knowing that she didn't have to continue to live in this perpetual mental torture.

With an eagerness that rivaled her son's when the ice cream truck came by, Ahmed began her treatment. By this point in time, Ahmed had decided to make a switch in her psychiatrist. "In my session with my first psychiatrist, I didn't have a great experience," she revealed. "I think it partially stemmed from his lack of cultural understanding. For example, he didn't understand why I felt compelled to quit my job and stay home—he simply viewed it as an outrageous thing for a woman to do in the twenty-first century." So, Ahmed started on a hunt to find a South Asian psychiatrist. "Ideally, I would have liked to find a woman, but I found a male doctor and it was such a wonderful fit. It was like night and day." No longer did Ahmed have to explain herself at every turn; her psychiatrist simply understood, being of a similar cultural background. It made for a more conducive session, allowing her to feel more comfortable to continue receiving mental health services.

For many Asian Americans, cultural gaps are often the foundation of a reluctance to continue—or even start—psychiatric treatment. When mental health professionals lack the cultural understanding, patients can quickly become frustrated or upset, as they find themselves continually having to justify or explain practices and/or stigmas associated with their background. "The cultural gap can cause unproductive sessions, halting the development of a strong patient-physician relationship," says Dr. Reddy. Even with licensed professionals or peer counselors, if there is a lack of cultural understanding between the provider and the patient, the patient will start to doubt the effectiveness of psychiatric help *in general.* In the best-case scenario, the patient will simply switch providers—as Ahmed did. In the worst case, they cease seeking treatment, doubtful that anyone would understand, letting their condition worsen (Kim, 2015). Hence, it is extremely important to not only increase cultural competency within mental health professionals, but to also have more Asian professionals available. Professionals of similar backgrounds will understand their patients to a greater degree, allowing for conversations and treatment to better align with the patient's culture and customs. Zilin, a current medical student at the University of Massachusetts, confirms the benefits of having more Asian providers. "Anybody would prefer someone who knows where you're coming from," she says in our interview. "Medical institutions don't have a good history in treating BIPOC [Black, Indigenous, and People of Color] patients. Thus, having professionals who look like them, speak the same language as them, have the same cultural background as them will help make them [individuals of the Asian community] feel more comfortable and likely to seek help."

Supported by her new, culturally sensitive South Asian psychiatrist, Ahmed started her medication schedule to treat her depressive symptoms. He also referred Ahmed to a therapist in order to encourage her to learn techniques to better manage her mental health and her anxiety. "It was an eye-opening experience," she said. "I started to recognize my own destructive thoughts and way of thinking." This awareness became a huge shift for Ahmed, allowing her to break free from her previous patterns of negative and anxious thoughts. And so, slowly (but surely) Ahmed's mental health started improving. Though it took months of progress and setbacks, the medication, combined with visits to her psychiatrist, eventually brought her out of that depressive and anxious state. No longer was she spending her time in bed, unwilling to see her friends; now, Ahmed looked forward to meeting with them and rediscovering the importance of those connections. Rather than having thoughts that centered around her children's impending deaths, Ahmed's mind settled into a relatively calm stream of thoughts—about the day, about her plans, about her work. Together, all these little changes culminated into a massive effect: Ahmed was finally able to achieve a state of mental well-being. Her voice became lighter, filled with hope. "I became alive, again."

When it came time for Ahmed to end her therapy sessions, she made sure to continue to practice the techniques she picked up from them. "I take my medication and I use the tools I learned from therapy," she said. "That consistency is key." It's a sentiment mental health professionals continue to emphasize. "Treatment adherence, or consistency," psychologist Dr. Deborah Serani writes in a January 2017 blog post, "is critical to recovery (...) [and] to maintain mental well-being. For many, once they begin to feel a bit better, they stop coming to sessions, or decide not to take medication anymore. The problem here is that while their symptoms have improved, the mood disorder is not at a management level. And as such, relapse occurs." That's why staying consistent and adhering to your treatment plan even after reaching that state of mental well-being is critical to the mental health journey.

THE ROAD TO RECOVERY CONTINUES

Today, at forty years old, Sara Ahmed continues to build upon her newfound sense of stability.

No longer constantly weighed down by feelings of depression and anxiety, Ahmed is now able to move through her day productively. With rosy cheeks that greet everyone with a smile, Ahmed's kindness is palpable. Even a short conversation with her leaves you feeling warm and welcomed; her voice is animated, while her eyes shine with genuine interest. Her laugh—full, but airy—is contagious. Her genuine enthusiasm to learn is even more so. Truly, from meeting new people to delving into local community work, Ahmed continues to establish herself as an integral member of society.

In fact, in the past few years, Ahmed has transformed into a fierce advocate for mental health within the South Asian community. From her articles on PopSugar or her blog to her posts on Instagram, Ahmed has broken the silence on mental health that has plagued many API communities. Whether about her experiences with postpartum depression, therapy, or psychiatric medication, Ahmed has never shied away from speaking the truth. Her words have unlocked a new sense of awareness and openness not only within herself, but also among the online community. She believes in sharing her experiences for those who may be struggling themselves—to show them that there is help out there, that the mental suffering *isn't* endless.

Though, that doesn't mean Ahmed no longer experiences mental health struggles.

There are still times when Ahmed finds herself in the throes of depression or caught in anxiety-inducing thoughts. But the difference between Ahmed nearly a decade ago and Ahmed now lies in her willingness to receive professional treatment and support when needed. She's no longer inhibited by the inability to recognize when her mental health is poor; she's no longer afraid to admit that she needs help.

"People really have to have an open heart—and an open thought process—to be accepting of something new like [mental illness]," said Ahmed. And it was true. Only by taking a leap of faith into the world of mental health can we find mental wellness, too.

THE BREAKTHROUGH BOX

Whether or not you're a parent, constantly struggling (mentally) to get through the day is not, and should never be, the norm. That's why it is important to recognize when you are struggling and accept that you need help. Though, when you come from a culture that systemically stigmatizes mental health and mental illness, it can be difficult to remove yourself from such a mindset. However, when you do, it opens a whole new world—one where you experience mental well-being.

CHAPTER 4

JAMES

———

"Just give me a second to put my things away."

The epitome of selfless, James was always ready to sacrifice his comfort for the betterment of others. I had seen that within the first few seconds of (virtually) meeting him. In order to ensure a quiet place for our call, he holed himself up in his car, tired from his university's research lab. Despite the nearly ninety-degree heat—which felt more like a hundred degrees because of Delaware's humidity—he just shrugged off his sweatshirt, tied up his shoulder-length black hair, and got comfortable in his seat.

"I'm ready now," he said, his voice gentle, taking on a trembling quality characteristic of a nervous man. In the background, there were sounds of shifting and the distinctive clatter of keys hitting the bottom of a car's cup holder.

The seat of his car gave a small groan as he brought his phone's microphone closer to his mouth.

I now had James's full attention—and full access to his story.

FAMILY TROUBLES, ACADEMIC PRESSURES: RECOUNTING JAMES'S CHILDHOOD

Queens Borough, New York City, New York.

Known for its ethnic vibrancy, Queens is home to the New York Mets baseball team and the annual US Open tennis tournament. Its residents—diverse both in heritage and in income—fill the varied urban landscape, from the beach haven of Rockaway to the upscale suburbia of Forest Hills. A quick ride on the subway through Queens brings residents and visitors alike a worldly experience. Every time the subway doors slide open, different languages and smells flood the passengers' senses; it's as if each stop is a gateway to a new country. Tucked behind Manhattan, Queens is only a tunnel drive away from the heart of New York City (Encyclopedia Britannica Online Ed, 2003). Residents could enjoy the bustle of New York City's epicenter but slink away to the quiet of Queens at night. Queen's borough was considered, by its residents, the best of New York.

It was also the place James called *home*.

"We lived in a neighborhood called Bellerose," James said. "It was a diverse neighborhood, but there were definitely quite a few Asians, including Southeast Asians [specifically, Indonesians] like me, there." Due to the neighborhood's diversity, James always felt welcomed. A sense of community existed in his street, with neighborhood dinners and quick chats with the local mailman being quite common. "I was quite outgoing when I lived there," reminisced James. "I remember how I would hang out with people on my block, going over to each other's houses." It was James's haven, a safe place where he felt welcomed by and close with everyone.

In second grade, however, that all changed.

Just when James was about to turn eight, his family made an abrupt move to Long Island, the densely populated island located at the eastern edge of New York City. "This was before a lot of Asians moved in," James said, laughing. "It was a little odd at first, to say the least." In stark contrast to Bellerose, Long Island did not enjoy a community-wide closeness. Despite the proximity of everyone's homes, neighbors kept to themselves, only seeking to interact with those already known to them. The only sense of community James had access to was within school. "We rarely, if ever, spoke to our neighbors or those who lived on my street," he explained.

While it may seem insignificant, these connections outside of family were extremely important to James.

"I didn't really have a great home life," James said softly, slightly uncomfortable at the admission. "Whenever I think back to my childhood, my parents, all I remember is a lot of fighting growing up." However, he was quick to add that it wasn't any fault of their own. "My family always accepted me, always wanted the best for me," he explained. "It was more the situation than anything else." In his family, constant tension was the norm—specifically among the adults. Whether it was the arguments between his parents or his paternal grandmother and his mom, there was rarely a moment of peace in the house. Over time, as James became older, his parents started to become less and less available to him. "My dad would work like crazy, working overtime and coming back late, because he didn't want to be home." James's mother was only marginally better. "She was there for me emotionally, but that's about it." The only one James felt he could truly rely on was his older brother. This was the one person James looked up to, could relate to; he was the one who guided him, helped him, put a band-aid on his cuts. "He was always there to take care of me," James said to me, his voice thick with emotion. "He was a very, *very* big part of my childhood."

Regardless of the less-than-ideal family dynamics, James knew this fighting couldn't go on for long. Unsurprisingly, it came to an end—with a divorce.

Just as James entered the sixth grade, his parents officially separated, marking the end of a nearly two-decades-long parental war. It was an odd period of time in his life, going between two households. "But," James remarked, reflecting, "it was probably for the better."

Though it took time, James slowly became accustomed to his new normal. The split visits between his father's and mother's houses, no longer accompanied by incessant fighting, allowed for him to develop a more loving relationship with the two. His parents now held a greater concern for James and his brother, rather than being consumed by their arguments. Before long, his parents' situation drifted to the back of his mind as he faced a new stage of life: high school.

"I had a pretty typical high school experience," James said, "but what I didn't realize at the time was how heavily it weighed on me." Caught up in his school culture of academic excellence, James kept himself busy all four years—volleyball in the fall, stage crew in the spring, jazz band, yearbook...the list was never-ending, and the time was never enough. "I would go to school early for a student government meeting and then stay late to prepare for a festival." Some days, he didn't even get home until eight or nine at night. "It was exhausting," James added, with a small laugh. James's schedule may sound hectic, but it wasn't a cause of concern to him and his parents. It was just him doing what was required for a prestigious college acceptance—and this attitude is becoming more and more typical for American teens today.

In the United States, where the race to college becomes more and more cutthroat with each passing academic year, students are taking on greater responsibility and even more commitments. No longer are days spent idly. Rather, students' schedules are filled with seven AP classes, club meetings during lunch, practice after school, and five hours' worth of homework—all in the pursuit of an acceptance to one of the nation's top universities. "Facing record-low acceptance at top colleges," Washington Post journalist Jennifer Breheny Wallace writes in a September 2019 article, "many students feel tremendous pressure to achieve and resume-build in all aspects of their young lives." Instead of taking time to explore the world and their independent interests, students pick and choose activities as a means to an end. Parents, coaches, and administrators—especially in high-ranking school districts— only add onto the perceived pressure, placing expectations on students to achieve, no matter the cost. However, in partaking in this rat race, students are overworking themselves to a point of burnout and decreased mental health (Wallace, 2019). That lack of downtime, combined with academic and social pressures, can put students in a vulnerable position.

James was one such student.

FALLING INTO THE ABYSS AND FACING THE MALE MENTAL HEALTH STIGMA

It started with an inability to fall asleep. His nights would be spent lying flat on his mattress, eyes open and mind vacant, but heart heavy. Every morning, an internal battle ensued as he fought to find the motivation to rise from bed. Throughout the day, for brief moments, he would recede into himself, disconnected from what was going on around him. He felt like a hollow shell, just going through the motions. However, it didn't affect his academic or personal life greatly, so James pushed it aside. "It wasn't until my girlfriend broke up with me," James revealed, "did it get worse." Suddenly, he found himself unable to stomach most meals. He would go to class, then try to come straight home, only to isolate himself in his room. He had little interest in spending time with friends or family, too preoccupied with his feelings of inadequacy and deep, inexplicable sadness. He felt like his world was falling apart.

Oftentimes, mental health issues are caused or exacerbated by "trigger" events. From the passing of a loved one to the end of a relationship, these events can cause the mind to spiral into the depths of depression or fill one with anxiety. Even major mental illnesses can manifest due to (often traumatic) events or life circumstances. Childhood abuse, social isolation, experiencing discrimination, being a long-term caretaker for someone, losing a job, being houseless, becoming bedridden, bullying—all of these factors can contribute to the development of a mental illness (Mind Infoline, 2017). Now, this list is non exhaustive. It doesn't come close to covering the wide range of events, circumstances, and experiences that can lead to poor mental health. Regardless, it's worth noting that it is extremely important we don't trivialize an individual's trigger. "People process events differently," Rama, a current fourth-year medical student (MS-4) at the University of California, San Francisco, says. "Just because someone's mental health episode or mental illness is triggered by something you wouldn't even blink at, doesn't mean they're 'overreacting' or are 'pretending.'" Similar to how we each have our own unique tastes and personalities, people have distinct thresholds for what they are able to handle. A certain event or circumstance will incite different reactions in different people. Thus, it is important to remember what they're experiencing is valid, and family and friends should work to provide a supportive environment for that individual, presenting resources and options for help.

Despite the growing severity of James's mental health symptoms, he was reluctant to seek out help. "It was difficult for me to admit that my mental health wasn't in the best state," James said. "Though," he added, "I could never really tell you why." While James remains unable to pinpoint the reason for his difficulties to seek help, Dr. Paige Lee, a licensed psychologist at the University of California, Berkeley, had some insights. "There is a cultural and gender-based expectation where men shouldn't be emotional," Dr. Lee states. "Many API communities have a strong cultural standard of stoicism, where you 'suck it up,' not 'air it out.'" From birth, for most men, it is not acceptable to be emotional; even as a child, they are supposed to represent pillars of strength, taught to remain unmoved by external factors. Thus, when they experience feelings of depression, anxiety, or other mood-based disorders, they're reluctant to seek out help, afraid of being seen as "weak." For the broader Asian community, however, there is an added layer to that stigmatization. "Men part of the API community," Dr. Lee says, "are often emasculated by society. How they're seen in films and social media—it creates an added, unnamed pressure within the community to try and be that 'stoic' and 'strong' person." As a result, Asian American men tend to ignore their mental health symptoms.

Despite being more likely to suffer from depression compared to their female counterparts, Asian American men exhibit help-seeking behavior at a lower rate. Unfortunately, when left untreated, mental illness can have grave complications. According to a report from SAMHSA (Substance Abuse and Mental Health Services), a higher percentage of

Asian Americans were admitted to emergency rooms for mental health episodes, compared to all other racial groups. Of those hospitalized, it was found that Asian Americans were 70 percent less likely to utilize inpatient services (Nadal and Kuramoto, 2016). These statistics reflect the larger pattern observed among Asian American boys and men: They are less likely to seek professional help for behavioral and mental health issues than all other racial groups. When they finally do seek help, it's usually at a point of extreme distress.

Luckily for James, his mental health symptoms did not reach a point of hospitalization, partly due to his high school's pro-mental health approach. "There was always so much awareness and education," James recounted. "Every year, in every class, we were always taught to go talk to the counselors if you needed help." Initially, James didn't believe he needed these resources, even though he was experiencing continued thoughts of hopelessness and feelings of intense sadness. As a man and as a student, he felt he was supposed to endure this mental agony. But as he slipped deeper and deeper into a depressive state, he finally realized he couldn't keep going on like this. "I had to do something," he said. And so, although still reluctant, James did the one thing his school always reminded him to do in times like these: talk to his high school counselor.

•••

One Friday afternoon, James shakily walked out of his last class of the day, bidding his classmates goodbye. Instead of heading to his usual meetings and practices, James made his way to the front office, slipping behind his school's reception desk. Down the gray floored corridor, third door on the right.

Mrs. Smith, school counselor, read the sign on the mahogany door. A bit of perspiration lined his forehead as the reality of the situation hit. Was he really about to do this? Go to his school counselor to talk about...*feelings?*

James's hand froze in front of the doorknob. *Was this really necessary?* He took a step back, hesitating. *No,* he thought, *I know there's something going on. I need help.* Before he could back out, James let out a quick breath and knocked against the door. Immediately, the door opened, revealing a stout lady. Her smile was soft.

"Come in," she said.

SCHOOL COUNSELORS: LIMITATIONS AND BENEFITS

"It wasn't necessarily the most helpful experience," James said, "but it allowed me to eventually get professional help." In his experience, his high school counselors weren't well-equipped to handle mental health issues. "There wasn't a whole lot they could do," he explained. "They had hundreds of kids to deal with—not only did they have to handle mental health, but also schedules, college admissions, things like that." Thus, the vast majority of the time, his counselors would simply refer students to a nearby licensed professional. Even in James's case, they did the same.

It's a constraint experienced by high school counselors across the nation. "Counselors unquestionably have unique training to help students deal with social and emotional issues," Kathy Reamy, a school counselor in La Plata, Maryland, states in an article on NEA News by Tim Walker, "but the services they provide are typically responsive and brief therapy in nature." After all, with high volumes of students to serve for a wide variety of tasks, America's high school counselors simply do not have the bandwidth to provide proper and prolonged mental health help. Nationwide, on average, each counselor is responsible for about five hundred students; the American School Counselor Association recommends only two hundred and fifty (Anderson and Cardoza, 2016). This leaves a significant portion of students unable to receive help, a reality that is alarming considering the increasing rates of depression, anxiety, self-harm, and suicide among adolescents (Nadal and Kuramoto, 2016). Especially in highly under-resourced schools, in which counselors (if the district even has one) are ill-equipped to deal with mental health crises and students are unable to afford professional services, the rates are even worse (Askarinam and National Journal, 2016).

James, at least, was lucky. Even though his counselors couldn't provide the help he needed, he knew his family would be able to afford the psychiatrist referred to him. "At first, I was reluctant," James said, "but I knew I needed the help. Even if they weren't able to facilitate my treatment, they did help me understand how getting professional help would be beneficial for me." Though it wasn't immediate, it was only by opening up to the possibility of needing help—and realizing that something wasn't quite right—did James begin his journey toward mental wellness. Now that his self-inflicted stigma and reluctance was no longer an issue, it left only one more barrier: his parents.

THE GRAND (MENTAL HEALTH) REVEAL

The day his parents received the call from his high school counselor remains a vivid memory in James's mind.

"I remember being nervous the entire weekend," he said. After that initial conversation with his counselor, Mrs. Smith, James found himself worrying about what his parents would think. Though he knew his parents were always supportive of him, he wasn't sure what their reaction would be. After all, up until this point, he had made no mention or indication that he was struggling with his mental health. For all his parents knew, he was just busy (and stressed) with school and extra-curriculars. He still (mostly) ate dinner, he still was getting good grades—to his parents, there was no real change in his behavior. To them, there was no cause for concern.

Or so they thought, as they would find out come Monday.

•••

That Monday night, James came home to both of his parents sitting at the dining table—a rare sight since their divorce. His father's face looked stern but concerned. His mother was nearby, wringing her hands in her usual nervous fashion. James's eyes widened ever so slightly as understanding dawned on him.

Slowly, he slid the backpack off his back, letting it land on the hardwood floor.

"Come here, son," his father called, gesturing to the empty chair next to him.

James slid into the chair slowly. He sat there quietly, waiting for his parents to speak, unsure about what would come out of their mouths.

"We got a call from your counselor," his father began, "and your mother and I wanted to talk to you about it." James held his breath, his brain working a mile a minute, playing the different scenarios of how this conversation would go. "She said you were struggling with your mental health, that you needed to see a psychiatrist or therapist. She even referred one to me." His father held his gaze. "Is this true?"

James broke eye contact, fiddling with his fingers. It was now or never.

"Yes," James said, his voice barely above a whisper. "I do need the help."

For a couple of seconds, there was only silence. Then, his father stood up from the table and lumbered over to him.

"Then it's settled," he said, placing a hand on James's shoulder. "I'll call the reference your counselor gave me first thing in the morning. We'll set up an appointment."

James lifted his eyes to his mother's across the table. She gave a soft smile.

"I'm sure it will help," she said. "It's worth a try."

•••

Looking back, James wasn't sure it would've worked out the way it did, if it was him revealing to his parents he needed professional mental health services. "I think if I reached out to my parents on my own, they would've been a lot more doubtful," hypothesized James. "But since it was my high school counselor calling, it made them feel like what was happening to me was a bit more serious—and that I actually needed help." As the perceived authority figure, James's counselor was able to provide the needed credence to his mental health issues. In this way, school counselors and other school professionals may be unwittingly playing the advocate for their students when reporting—an important role that allowed James to access professional help.

TRYING THERAPY

Two weeks later, James found himself standing in front of a large glass door, with his father beside him. As promised, his father had made an appointment with the therapist. Though unsure, James was looking forward to the help—and hopefully, the relief.

"Thankfully," he said, "my experience was a positive one." From the first session, James immediately felt comfortable, welcomed, and respected by his therapist. The sessions were immensely helpful, providing him with tools and resources to use in his day-to-day activities. It was a place of active healing. "What I liked the most was how he [my therapist] didn't believe in labels. I wasn't a 'depressed teenager.' Rather, I was a teen with a different set of problems I had to work through. And that was it." It was a refreshing take that enabled James to feel less overwhelmed with his mental health diagnosis. It was no longer this "big" mental illness he had to overcome, but rather a handful of symptoms that he could work to treat.

In the beginning, James would visit his therapist *and* his high school counselors. This way, he could receive support both in and out of school, especially since his therapy sessions were only twice a month (once every other week). However, he eventually ceased visiting his counselors, due to a particular incident. "There was this one time," James recounted, "when I was at the counselor. I was just hoping to talk through what I was experiencing, but my counselor instead called up my father—in front of me, despite my denials." While his counselors were only following protocol (as they are legally obligated to report when they believe the student is posing a threat to themselves or others), it was a bit of a traumatizing experience for James. "While my parents were supportive of me going to therapy, they hadn't come face to face with one of my mental health episodes. I preferred keeping it that way—I wasn't ready for anything otherwise." To have his innermost thoughts and experiences told to his parents in excruciating detail was one of the most unpleasant experiences in his life. James's face became grim. "I didn't visit my counselors after that."

Instead, he opted to visit his therapist more frequently—on a weekly basis, to be exact. "Over the course of my treatment, I started seeing some improvement," James told me. Although his depressive thoughts did not disappear, he now had the understanding, tools, resources, and support to help keep those intrusive thoughts and feelings at bay. These skills were invaluable to James, especially on the days when his depression seemed to almost get the best of him. However, even after a whole year of therapy, many of his symptoms persisted. Thus, his therapist recommended he visit his psychiatrist to start on medication.

"My parents and I were quick on going to therapy," said James, "but we were a lot more hesitant with medication." Using medication to treat an invisible illness was a foreign concept to his family. Therapy was one thing, but medication? It was a terrifying option, especially to his parents. "Faith, mindfulness techniques—those were legitimate courses of action to any mental health issues, to both my parents and myself. Medication, on the other hand, was deemed as unnecessary."

That's why, at first, his family resisted. "We thought I just needed to go to therapy more, to try harder." But with college around the corner—and no end to James's depression in sight—he and his parents started to consider it. If therapy wasn't bringing significant improvement on its own, perhaps medication would be the best next step.

So, in the summer before college, James's parents tentatively booked an appointment with a psychiatrist.

A LEAP INTO THE UNKNOWN: MEDICATION AS A TOOL FOR RECOVERY

"This wasn't our first time at the psychiatrist," said James. "But it was definitely our first time going to the psychiatrist with the serious intention of considering medication as a treatment option." What ensued was a slew of questions, diagnostics, and evaluations. The psychiatrist wanted to see if medication was truly necessary; James and his parents wanted to see if medication would truly help. In the end, through a series of appointments and conversations, they were able to come to a consensus: They would go ahead with the medication.

"I was prescribed mild depressive medication. Thankfully, I didn't experience any drastic side effects." Instead, what he saw was a vast improvement in his mental health. "While therapy was helpful, it wasn't until I started medication that I truly felt *better*." If depression was a mental fog, therapy was the fog light that helped him see through it. While therapy helped James *manage* his symptoms, it didn't eradicate any of them. Medication, however, was the warmth of sunlight that cleared the majority of that depressive fog. It ended up alleviating the majority of the symptoms James faced. "It was a game-changer for me."

LOOKING BACK AND LOOKING AHEAD

Today, with his medication and his therapist, James is able to live his life without the same heaviness and difficulty that plagued his high school years. "Now, I'm able to manage my depressive symptoms as they come. Instead of spiraling in isolation, I now am able to use the resources and tools I need to feel better." To get to this point, however, wasn't easy.

No one was able to identify nor understand what James was going through. And how could they? Others didn't have access to his innermost thoughts and feelings. Even if they did somehow realize and reach out, it was unlikely he would've sought out the resources; unless James himself was ready to accept that possibility, it would've been almost impossible to convince him to get treatment. After all, the first step of any mental health journey is self-realization and self-acceptance.

Unsurprisingly, James's road to recovery only began after that initial realization. After becoming aware of his own mental state, admitting he was struggling, and understanding he needed outside help, James went to his counselors—ultimately unlocking a host of resources and professional services. "It changed the course of my life and my outlook on mental health," James said as he reflected on his mental health journey thus far. He laughed lightly. "And I'll forever be thankful to myself for that."

THE BREAKTHROUGH BOX

As a boy or a man, it is not weak to admit that you need help. Though the wider AAPI culture/community places expectations of stoicism and endurance on their boys and men, it is important to remember that true strength comes from recognizing and admitting you need help.

And for those not a part of the Asian/Pacific Islander communities, understand there are unique barriers that can prevent an individual from easily seeking help. So, regard them with compassion.

PART 2

SUPPORT SYSTEM AND RESOURCES

Whether working toward recovery or healing or an award, having support transforms what once seemed like a daunting task into an attainable goal. While self-reliance is important and admirable, uphill battles become that much more manageable when we open ourselves to help.

It's the same for any individual's mental health journey. Neither mental health nor mental illness is meant to be dealt with alone. Learning to lean on others, seeking help from those around you, utilizing the resources that are available to you—these are all necessary when striving for mental wellness. Halima Khan and Sonya remind us of that.

For the two of them, healing and recovery weren't achieved when they tried to manage their mental health symptoms by themselves. Rather, only when they looked to outside resources and decided to trust those close to them did they get to where they are today.

As Sonya and Khan show us, true strength doesn't just come from within; it also comes from relying on others, even when being vulnerable and asking for help makes us feel weak. It comes from recognizing that we cannot do it alone, that we need resources and support. It comes from pushing forward in the face of failed attempts at recovery, not giving up until we find what helps us achieve mental wellness.

Whether you're the one reaching out or the one supporting, it will always be a team effort.

CHAPTER 5

HALIMA KHAN

"I was eleven years old when it started."

At first glance, Halima Khan seemed like a quiet, timid individual. Though her smile was bright, she grasped at her hair in a nervous fashion as she surveyed me with cautious eyes. Her dark brown, nearly black hair was straightened to perfection, her lips were shiny with lip gloss, and her tan skin was smoothed down with foundation. There was a certain softness about her, which was only accentuated by what she was wearing: a pastel pink dress and a cream-colored hijab that framed her rosy cheeks.

Suddenly, Khan's cat hopped into frame, settling into her lap. "Her name is Almira," Khan said, letting out a little laugh as she stroked Almira's furry back lovingly. Cat still in hand, Khan settled into the corner of her bed, folding her legs underneath. Her back remained stiff against her beige walls, which were decorated with posters and pictures of nature. The nightstand beside her bed frame was painted white, a vase of yellow roses set on top. Unlike the floral decorations by her bed, her dresser and desk were completely covered with various knickknacks and mementos of her travels, indicative of her sentimental nature.

"I'm honestly just counting down the days till I can get to campus," she informed me. At eighteen years old, the COVID-19 pandemic had put a damper on many of the plans Khan had for the summer before her first year of college, but that didn't stop her from making the most of the remaining few months she had before she departed for the fall. With the newfound free time, she decided to apply for a job at the local mall as a way to offset the cost of tuition. When not setting up the store's displays or ringing up satisfied customers, Khan spent her time binging the latest K-dramas on Netflix and setting up photoshoots with her pet.

As part of her town's South Asian Muslim community, Khan (similar to her other Muslim peers) was often the subject of much scrutiny growing up—a reality that she seemed to always endure with humility and grace. She attended each and every prayer, dressed modestly, and donned a hijab. In such a small, suburban town filled with a high Asian and Islam-practicing population, this kind of pressure and scrutiny seemed imminent, although, from the outside, it didn't seem to be much of a problem for Khan.

The inside, however, held a much different story.

IT BEGINS IN MIDDLE SCHOOL

Middle school is usually supposed to be an awkward time of self-discovery and gangly limbs. Defined by first crushes and worries for the next pop quiz, middle school is known as the quintessential bridge between elementary and high school. In Khan's hometown, it was all that and more.

Located in Southern California, Khan lived in a town known for its relatively close proximity to the beach. Within the past decade, it has rapidly developed into an up-and-coming hub of first-generation Asian immigrants, slowly creating an environment complete with high-stakes academic pressure and above-average performance.

A quick look into any of the community's middle schools reveals tendencies seen in many affluent, suburban towns. Students start to join clubs and activities, trying to understand where their interests and passions lie in time for high school. They begin to get accustomed to "periods" and "bell schedules," in which they learn to rotate between teachers and classes. Weekends are filled with big games, SAT prep, and sleepovers, while weekdays are spent puzzling through math homework. This constant stream of activities was typical.

Khan's experiences, however, were radically different.

"I would come home, only to lock myself in my room and start hysterically crying," she said.

Along with intense feelings of sadness and hopelessness, Khan started to exhibit many other signs of a mental health disorder: an inability to fall asleep, a severe lack of motivation, and fatigue. Her afternoons would be spent lying in bed, nursing a raging headache that just never seemed to leave, and her nights would be filled with self-harm and endless thoughts of suicide. She would even starve herself, uncaring about the consequences. "I hated myself then."

Middle school was a turbulent time for Khan, as she didn't completely understand what was going on. "All I knew is that I kept feeling helpless and lost," she said. "From my knowledge, others my age weren't dealing with the same kinds of feelings and things I was going through. So, I kept it all to myself, never trying to understand my struggle." For two years, Khan continued with her self-harming behavior, trapped in the cycle of low self-worth and extreme negative feelings. It wasn't until the end of middle school, when she was only a year away from starting high school, that she attempted to look into why she felt so low. "I noticed none of my other friends were hiding the scars on their forearms or wrists," she explained. "They moved through life happily, excitedly, filled with energy. So, I started to wonder why I wasn't able to do the same."

After a quick search on the internet about her symptoms and thoughts, Khan came across what it could be: depression.

RISING FEARS

The realization was both comforting and terrifying to her. On one hand, she finally had a name to what she was experiencing; on the other, she knew that mental illness was seen as a taboo topic in her community.

Khan debated going to her parents. She wasn't sure how they would react—and worse, she was afraid of how her community would act if they found out something might be "wrong" with her.

"I had seen how my community reacted when a friend of mine came out about her depression," Khan told me. "Everyone, my parents included, immediately shunned her. I distinctly remember how my parents would repeatedly warn me not to hang out with her." Despite suffering from depression all her life, Khan's friend wasn't treated as an "other" until she became public with her diagnosis. "Families would just excuse her behavior, seeing her as a little odd, but nothing to be distanced from," Khan said, "but the minute there was a name to her behavior—depression, in this case—people avoided her like the plague."

The connotations and stereotypes associated with mental illnesses like depression led to this reaction, and it's an occurrence that is all too common in many API communities, whether in the United States or abroad. "For Asian communities, that stigma kicks in, causing people to not be very receptive to those who are opening up about their mental illness," Ragini Lal of NAMI-CA revealed to me in an interview. The severe lack of education and high spread of misinformation about mental health and mental illness contribute to that stigma. Even among those of us who may be informed and educated about mental health, it becomes difficult to suddenly change the very behaviors and let go of the viewpoints that were modeled from birth; further, the cultural precedents leave people reluctant to question the established status quo, in fear of the backlash on themselves or their families. But for many of our communities, the alienation of those with a mental illness comes from not understanding *what* mental illness is and *how* it manifests. Some families assume mental health struggles are indicative of the parents' inability to provide; others, relying on stereotypes of extreme cases of mental illness, automatically equate it with "craziness," or a "lack of sanity." While environmental circumstances (including the quality of one's home life) certainly do play a role in the development of mental illness, it isn't a universal attributing factor—nor should it be the source of judgment toward a family or an individual. In doing so, we run the risk of creating an environment where people are afraid of being open about their experiences—a reality we already see today.

STRIVING TOWARD COMPREHENSIVE MENTAL HEALTH EDUCATION

With the stigma weighing down on her, Khan was a bit lost on where to go and who to turn to. "When you're in middle school, there isn't much of a conversation about mental health and mental illness," she said. "So, I didn't even know what resources were available to me, nor where I could go to access them. It had already taken me so long to realize I had depression, but now that I had, I didn't know where to turn to."

In the state of California, school districts that received federal funding were not required to incorporate suicide and mental health education and awareness in their courses. In 2012, when Khan was a mere sixth grader in middle school, there wasn't even a government mandate to adopt suicide prevention and training policies for the district and their staff. It wasn't until 2017, under Assembly Bill 2246, that suicide and mental health education, training, and awareness became required by school districts. Since 2017, schools that serve grades seven and above are now required to ensure their staff are trained to handle mental health crises, while actively working towards the "prevention, intervention, and postvention (sometimes called the 'aftermath')" of suicide. Starting from mid- to late-2020, some school districts (specifically, those in San Diego County) will also be piloting a program—LivingWorks Start—to provide their middle school and high school *students* with suicide prevention training (California Department of Education, 2020).

While this is a step forward in the right direction, many middle and high schools still aren't equipping themselves with the right tools to educate their students about the broad nature of mental health and mental illness. Ragini Lal provides her insights on this: "For years now, we have had a problem with pregnancies and too many children, which translated into increased sex education at an early age. It should be the same for mental illness." In the United States, suicide is listed as the second-highest cause of death for ages ten to twenty-four (Heron, 2019). When children are getting to that low point at such a young age, it is indicative of a struggle that started years prior, likely during elementary or middle school. "On top of that, the age of people being diagnosed with mental illness goes as young as three or four years old—and I'm talking about depression or anxiety," Ragini Lal states. "This just shows us how important it is to educate as early as possible." And it makes sense; when we have sex education to prevent pregnancies, we should have mental health education to prevent suicides and generate a better understanding of mental health and mental illness. The lack of education—and the lack of dissemination of the available resources—severely limits how easily students can get the help they may need. While some say that education will only cause a "bandwagon approach," in which impressionable students may "think themselves into" a mental illness where there isn't one, I argue that these rare one percent of cases shouldn't stop us from helping the ninety-nine percent that is *actually* suffering. In the pursuit of preventing the few copycat cases, we'd be allowing hundreds of thousands of students to slip through the cracks. We shouldn't accept that. Without that awareness, students are unable to understand that what they might be feeling and experiencing could be a sign of a mental illness—ultimately delaying their access to said resources.

THE ONLINE COMMUNITY CAN BE YOUR FRIEND

Being unable to turn to her family or her school, Khan ended up relying on the internet to get the support she needed. By joining various online networks and platforms that catered to those who were struggling with their mental health, she found a sense of community, support, and acceptance. The virtual world became a place for her to share her highs and her lows while gaining access to various resources to help her manage her depression. They reminded her to eat every day and often talked her out of self-harm.

Although Khan's experiences with the online community remained generally positive, Dr. Lee of the University of California, Berkeley, had a few words of advice on this. "As long as the online resource or community is effective and seems to be helping, that's great! I encourage you to use it. But if it's making things worse, then I might think twice about whether this is really helping you." According to NAMI (n.d.), the use of online therapy and support groups is becoming increasingly popular, as it offers a "convenience and accessibility that in-person therapy may not be able to provide." However, it can take some trial and error to find the group or service that best meets your needs (NAMI, n.d.). Ultimately, while the online community can be a great place of support, it is important to remain wary and tread forward with caution. All it takes is one internet troll or a toxic online community to ruin any progress you might have been making. "While it's important to get creative when your resources are limited," Dr. Lee concludes, "you should always evaluate the community or resource on whether it is making things better—or worse. Are you healing? Or are you hurting from it?"

For Khan, the online communities were her salvation. They allowed her to feel connected and not so alone. "For some time," Khan said, her mouth turned into a sad smile, "it worked." Then, just as Khan thought she was getting better, she got much, much worse.

A TURNING POINT BROUGHT UPON BY TRAGEDY
On January 2, 2016, Halima Khan was rushed to the hospital for severe self-inflicted injuries and attempted suicide.

Her parents had walked into her room, only to find Khan collapsed and bleeding profusely from her wrists, a glass shard balanced loosely in her hand. "I had hit my lowest point, by then," Khan said. "The pressures of high school just compounded on my feelings of worthlessness, and my mental health became hell. I no longer felt like my life was worth living."

Academic and social pressures are known to have a negative effect on student well-being and mental health; the Asian American community is no exception. Coming from a culture where excellence is prioritized, children, teens, and young adults from this community often become susceptible to increased risk of suicide, depression, anxiety, and other mental health disorders. "The expectations, [whether it is] criticizing appearance, comparing successes, or not being [*blank*] enough, impacts the mental health of AAPI's," Mental Health America writes on their website (2021). With an emphasis on "honor to the family," Asian cultures inadvertently create and place pressures on children to achieve, which, when left unchecked, can become extremely harmful to the child's mental health (Mental Health America, 2021). In Khan's situation, the stress and the pressures of appearing perfect in front of her cultural community worsened her depression. "My parents, like many other Asian parents, expected me to be the very best—in the religious, academic, and social sense," she said, "and whenever I slipped up in any of those aspects, I felt like I had failed my parents and my family. It became a source of my self-hatred, not that my parents knew that."

And they didn't know, not until the day they discovered Khan's seemingly lifeless body on the bedroom floor. After being treated for her injuries, Khan was evaluated by the resident psychiatrist, answering a series of questions and completing various standardized questionnaires measuring her mood. Her official diagnosis? Clinical depression.

"When I heard that diagnosis, I literally broke down into tears," Khan revealed to me. "I felt validated. Finally, this professional—this *doctor*—validated everything I had been feeling and experiencing for the past four years." She paused, looking at me with tears in her eyes. "I felt *seen*," she said.

Clinical depression, also known as major depressive disorder or major depression, is a serious but common mental illness. In fact, as of 2017, nearly 7.1 percent of adults and 13.3 percent of children were reported to have experienced a clinical depression episode in the United States (National Institute of Mental Health, 2019). Among the AAPI population, it is estimated that between 4.5 percent and 11.3 percent of adults exhibit major depression, with adolescent girls having the highest rates of depressive symptoms (Kim et al., 2015; NAMI Multicultural & International Outreach Center, 2004).

Despite its commonality, the symptoms experienced can vary from individual to individual. They can include persistent feelings of sadness, anxiousness or emptiness, irritability (a symptom more common in children and adolescents), fatigue, restlessness, difficulty concentrating or remembering, difficulty sleeping or oversleeping, appetite or weight changes, thoughts of suicide or suicide attempts, and body aches/headaches or cramps without an apparent cause. When a combination of these symptoms, along with persistent low mood, are experienced continuously for at least two weeks, it is considered clinical depression (National Institute of Mental Health, 2018), which was exactly the case for Khan.

Shortly after her diagnosis, Khan was recommended, then admitted to a psychiatric hospital in order to treat her underlying mental health issues. Despite struggling with her mental health since she was eleven years old, this was the first time Khan had been able to access professional mental health services. The fact that she only received professional help when things got dire doesn't come as a surprise to most mental health professionals.

"There is a huge population of Asian Americans who don't receive treatment until it becomes an emergency," Dr. Hsu reveals in Episode 31 of *Emil Amok's Takeout,* a podcast hosted by Emil Guillermo in association with the Asian American Legal Defense and Education Fund (2018). "Even in [affluent] places, the first contact Asian Americans have with mental health professionals are during emergencies." In fact, as Dr. Fan of the University of Massachusetts Medical School found in a research study, it was more common to see Asian Americans with mental health disorders when things got dire, like in the emergency room or among hospitalized patients (Wu et al., 2018). "In Asian cultures in general," psychiatrist Dr. Fan explains in an April 2018 article by Cristina Quinn, "when someone is talking about emotional experiences, psychological disturbances and challenges, it's considered a character defect or personal weakness." Thus, Asian Americans tend to "silently endure it," not reaching out to trusted adults, nor their community, for help; like in Khan's case, it is all a consequence of the stigma, as well as the severe lack of information on the available resources (Quinn, 2018).

But no matter how dire it gets, stigma is always hard to shake off. In the end, Khan was pulled out of the facility before the end of her psychiatric treatment. Within three days, her parents refused to allow her to continue treatment at the hospital, as they believed their daughter "wasn't crazy enough" to need institutional intervention. "There is a strong stigma held towards psychiatric hospitals and institutions," Khan explained. "In my family and in my community, if you go there, it means you're not sane at all."

But once they came home, Khan fought with her parents. In her brief time at the psychiatric hospital, she had found relief and help and support. "For the second time in my life, I found a place—a community, really—that could help me. For once in my life, I *wanted* to be helped. I *wanted* to get better." It was days on end with screaming matches and angry tears, as father and daughter argued about what her next steps were. Khan's father, like many Asian immigrants, didn't believe in the traditional resources and help promoted in the United States; instead, he wanted his daughter to turn to their religion, Islam, for the support and guidance to endure what he saw as a temporary test from God. (While these beliefs can be comforting and helpful for many individuals, we must be careful to realize that it isn't necessarily the best solution for everyone.)

This perception Khan's father had toward mental illness was one that many Asian communities hold; many families explain away and seek solutions to mental health issues through *some* factor of their observed religion. For example, in Hindu culture, mental illness is seen as a result of a "karmic debt" (debt that incurs from past lives) that needs to be repaid. It's usually regarded as a consequence of a sinful past life. This viewpoint is exemplified by a 1986 study in India, in which researchers surveyed 150 Indian patients with various mental illnesses (ranging from schizophrenia to mania to depression), asking who or what the individual blamed for their mental illness. The vast majority answered that the self (specifically, the past self) was to blame, viewing their current "predicament" as punishment for their past life's actions (Narayanan et al., 1986). As such, the majority of these individuals believed religion, prayer, and accumulating "good" karma would be the key to alleviating their mental health symptoms and preventing mental illness in future lives—not antipsychotic medication, antidepressants, or a counselor. It was the same for Khan's family, in regard to them not believing in Western treatments like therapy and medication.

"I had a hard time trying to convince [my father] and my mom to allow me to get professional help," she said. "They didn't understand why I was experiencing mental health struggles and didn't believe that the resources out there would help. Plus, they were terrified that if we went and sought out help, someone outside of our family would find out." Despite their reservations, it was Khan's persistence that won them over. In the end, her parents agreed to seek out a therapist for her, but on one condition: they must approve of the therapist first.

"I knew that meant I probably wouldn't be connected with a therapist until much later," she said, "but that was a risk I was willing to take. At least they were ready to get me professional help."

And so, the search began.

HOW THE PROFESSIONAL HELP BACKFIRED

For weeks, the Khan family searched for an affordable therapist. They visited multiple offices and therapists, ultimately settling on one in the town over, about thirty minutes away. "The biggest reason my parents were the most comfortable to take me to this therapist was because she was Muslim, like us," Khan recounted. And it made sense. As Dr. Hsu of Stanford University says in *Emil Amok's Takeout*, Asian Americans—specifically, older Asian Americans—tend to feel more comfortable receiving mental health help when the professional is of similar background (2018). This rings true for when their child is the one seeking help as well.

The reason lies in the viewpoint many Asian Americans hold toward mental health, Dr. Hsu explains. For many, mental health struggles are often seen as a "white people thing." With many white Americans often more willing to seek professional help for their mental health struggles, Asian Americans have come to associate mental health and mental illness with their white counterparts. To many people from this community, it isn't seen as something that affects the Asian race. Thus, in connecting with a mental health professional from a similar ethnic background, the notion that it only affects white Americans starts to diminish. Individuals, now feeling more secure in the competence of the professional, start to understand mental health can affect Asians as well, becoming more ready to seek help themselves. Not to mention, having a mental health professional of similar ethnic background helps to bridge that cultural gap that often occurs with a white therapist or psychiatrist.

However, for Khan, the Muslim therapist ended up harming, rather than helping, her. "In my first therapy session with her, after I had talked to her about everything I had been feeling for the past couple of years, the first thing she told me was to 'pray more,'" Khan revealed. "In that moment, I never felt more dismissed and humiliated in my life." As a devout Muslim, Khan already heavily incorporated prayer into her day, performing *namaz* (Islamic prayer) five times a day. However, for Khan, the routine prayers did little to alleviate her mental health struggles—she needed more than that. She needed somebody to listen, to provide the appropriate resources, and to equip her with the tools to better handle her mental health and depression. The last thing she wanted was someone to tell her to "pray more," questioning her commitment to her religion while simultaneously chalking up her struggles to a lack of faith.

Immediately, Khan stormed out of the room, tears in her eyes. She stalked over to where her parents were waiting, demanding that they go home. "I didn't want to be in that office for even a second longer." Without waiting to explain, she left the clinic, her parents trailing behind confused. Once home, her parents, bewildered by her reaction, asked what was wrong. Still upset and trembling with anger, Khan recounted what the therapist had told her. Her parents patiently listened, their brows furrowing in concern. However, once she was done revealing why, her parents merely blinked at her blankly, not understanding the issue. "To them, the advice to 'pray more' made sense," Khan explained. "Religion is a huge part of our lives, so they saw it as a viable solution."

Despite Khan's refusal to return, her parents were insistent that she gives the therapist another chance. To them, the therapist met all their requirements: Muslim, close by, and affordable. One little comment shouldn't matter so much, right?

"But it *did* matter," Khan admitted. "What the therapist said bothered me—but, in the end, I decided to give her another try, since she seemed to be the only one my parents were willing to take me to."

Reluctantly, Khan made her way back to the clinic the next week. "In the back of my mind, I was kind of grateful," she said. For the longest time, she had denied her experiences and symptoms, unable and unwilling to get the help she clearly needed. Afraid of how her parents would react, she kept her struggles hidden, attempting to deal with them on her own—until she no longer could. "Here were my parents, pushing me to get help—even if that therapist wasn't the best, it *was* help." However, before Khan could even set a foot into the office, her parents were dragging her out. "When we entered the clinic's waiting room, we saw someone we knew—a family friend," Khan said. "Immediately, my parents freaked."

In a blind panic, her parents left the premises, rushing into their car and out of the parking lot. As they made their way back home, her mother watched out the passenger-side window, her face strained with fear and apprehension; her father gripped the steering wheel tightly, his mouth set into a grim line. The entire car hummed with tension—all because of a familiar face. "I still remember how quiet the car ride home was," Khan said. "And in that moment, I knew we wouldn't be going to that therapist any longer." In fact, as she quickly discovered, they wouldn't be going to any therapist ever again.

LOG KYA KAHENGE?

To Khan's parents, in that singular moment, their worst fears had been realized: someone outside of their family of five knew their "*dirty little secret.*" Someone was now aware of their daughter's mental illness—and knew she was seeking out mental health services. It was a reality that was met with abject horror, as their minds became plagued by one thought: *Log kya kahenge? What will other people think?*

"That's the first thing parents usually think of when it comes to their children," Khan explained. Although the term "Asian" encompasses a wide variety of cultures and ethnicities, there seems to be one common thread that ties them together: collectivism. In contrast with Western nations, many Asian countries and cultures emphasize the collective over the individual. Thus, a family's "success" is dependent on each member of the "group," including their own children. Considering that mental health and mental illness hold a strong negative stigma within these communities, it comes as no surprise that families take extreme measures to hide their children's mental health diagnoses from others. "Once it [news about mental health] gets out in the community, it becomes a huge mess," Khan elaborated. "And they [the parents] don't want to carry that mess on their shoulders. They don't want to have that reputation. They only want to be known as that perfect, successful family."

Despite her continued pleading, Khan's parents refused to seek out other therapists. Their brief encounter with their family friend at the clinic was enough to cease their searching. It reminded them of the shame that would befall the family if news of her depression got out to the community at large. With their family's reputation on the line, it was a risk they weren't ready to take, as their community wasn't ready to accept mental illness as a regular facet of humanity.

SEEKING (ALTERNATIVE) SOLUTIONS
Despite the new roadblock to accessing mental health services for her depression, Khan was determined not to revert to her mental state prior to hospitalization. Instead, she

decided to gather the support and resources she needed to maintain her mental health—starting with her friends and the internet.

After dealing with her mental illness in private for five years, Khan started opening up to her closest friends about her struggles. "I turned to those who I found to be particularly understanding and empathetic," she stated. "After I opened up to them, I immediately received a flood of support. It was liberating, not having to keep it to myself all the time." From that point on, whenever she felt her mental health start to deteriorate, she practiced reaching out to these individuals. "I would just call them up—sometimes even crying—and talk to them about what I was feeling," Khan revealed. "It felt foreign at first, learning to rely on others for that help and support, especially when sometimes there was no specific reason for why I was so sad." However, she continued to force herself to reach out to them, until it became natural for her to do so.

Over time, these individuals evolved into her established support system, always encouraging her to reach out to them whenever she felt hopeless or low.

Today, Khan's support system continues to play an integral role in her life. From periodically checking in on Khan to making sure she's eating daily, her support system is always there to remind her to prioritize her mental health and mental well-being. However, friends are not the only resource she turns to when caught in the cycle of self-hatred and depression. She also utilizes the free tools that are shared online (some of which are linked at the end of the book, under "Resources for Further Exploration").

"Whether it is a 'mindfulness' video or an online support group that shares tips on how to handle depressive episodes, the internet has been a huge asset to my mental health," she said. These online resources are only a search away, with various mental health organizations and initiatives providing free resources to manage mental health disorders, including mood disorders and anxiety. These same websites and social media accounts also often contain tools to help manage mental health episodes, as well as reminders that promote mental wellness. From organizations like Mental Health America, which contains various resources specific to the API community, to social media accounts like *Subtle Asian Mental Health* (@subtleasianmentalhealth) and *Asian Mental Health Collective* (@asianmentalhealthcollective) on Instagram, there are a wide plethora of resources, tools, and support people can access. It's merely a matter of finding the ones that help and incorporating them into your life.

"Especially when you don't have access to professional mental health services, the online world can be an immensely useful avenue to acquire the needed help and resources," Dr. Lee states. Various mental health professionals echo the same sentiment, emphasizing the importance of receiving some form of help, rather than none at all; finding healthy outlets and resources that improve your mental health is worth searching for. Although it took time, practice, and a lot of research, the support system and the online resources Khan has curated have become valuable substitutes. "Without them, I don't know where I'd be today," Khan told me, her eyes shining with a sense of hope and self-assurance. After hearing her story, that hope was definitely a beautiful sight.

REFLECTIONS ON HER MENTAL HEALTH JOURNEY
Seven years ago, Halima Khan was battling some of her worst depressive episodes, with no help, people, or resources to

turn to. Four years ago, her depression, coupled with the crippling pressures of school and society, had brought her to her lowest place—her bedroom floor, with a glass shard in hand. Today, although there are days she finds it difficult to even get out of bed, Khan is no longer dealing with her mental illness on her own. Surrounded by those who support and love her (as well as a therapist and parents who now better understand the importance of therapy), and armed with the tools to help her, Khan is an example of how persistence is the key to finding the help and the resources that best fit your mental health needs. Without these resources or that support system, it can become difficult to maintain mental wellness and manage mental health symptoms. Khan knows that better than most.

"The one thing I've learned from my mental health journey is to never give up," Khan said. "Even when it feels like nothing can help you, I'm here to tell you, there is. Find your support system, search for your resources, especially when you can't get professional help. Keep looking, until you find what works for you—because I *promise* you, something will."

THE BREAKTHROUGH BOX

Don't give up on finding your resources. It is never a waste of time to find the help that works best for you, whether it is therapy, meditation, or support groups.

And if you know someone who is unable to utilize professional services, don't be afraid to be a support for them. Sometimes, that in itself can make a world of difference.

CHAPTER 6

SONYA

———

She sat on the kitchen counter, the coolness of the black and brown speckled granite pressing against her face. A tear slowly pooled at the corner of her eye, then slid down her tan cheek. An empty plate, save for a few crumbles, was next to her on the countertop. Without even thinking about it, she swiped her finger along the surface of the plate, bringing the collected crumbs to her mouth. Suddenly, she paused, reality hitting her. Tears now flowed down her cheek in rapid succession. The momentary bliss she felt when consuming the *gulab jamun* was long gone. Now she was riddled with not only the sadness from her doctor's visit last week, but also with the guilt of eating uncontrollably—*again.*

It was a scene that had become all too common for Sonya during her sophomore year of high school. At fifteen years old, Sonya was trapped in a toxic cycle of emotional eating and guilt. Days that were once filled with carefree afternoons at friends' houses were now spent alone in the refuge of her home. The confidence she once had was now replaced by intense insecurity with herself and her body. The food that once connected her to her family was now her mortal enemy.

There seemed to be no escape for her—*or so she thought.*

CULTIVATING A CULTURAL CONNECTION THROUGH FOOD

"I didn't always have a problematic relationship with food," Sonya tells me. "But I did always have a close one."

For Sonya, food was always her home. As a young South Asian girl, her mother and relatives would hold out bites of *dosas* and *laddu* throughout the day. Mealtime was always accompanied by encouragement to take another plate of rice—with curry, of course. To say "no" to these offers was incomprehensible. These dishes were her family's way of declaring their love; eating was Sonya's way of showing the love back. But more than anything, it was a way for her to stay connected with her family and culture.

"When we moved to San Jose [a city in California] at the beginning of middle school, my mother was always busy with work," she said. "My mom and I would be unable to go to the local cultural events, not that it really mattered." Living in such an academically competitive town meant there was little done to build true community among residents; cultural celebrations were marred by conversations between parents about their child's achievements. Of the few events she and her mother would attend, nearly all were mere excuses to draw comparisons between the children. So, over time, Sonya and her mother completely opted out of these excursions. "Instead, my weeks became filled with homework, school, extracurriculars—and nothing more."

As a result, without any real connection to her culture, Sonya found herself feeling increasingly isolated. "I felt like I was losing my culture, my happiness." The only line that remained was that through food.

It wasn't always like this, however.

"When I was young, in elementary school, there would always be weekly cultural events my family would attend." On the days her mom was too swamped with work, Sonya's grandparents would accompany her to the neighborhood get-togethers, where families would bring homemade South Asian dishes. Hindu festivals weren't just "boring" at-home *poojas,* but community-wide events. Parents wouldn't discuss or compare their children, but rather educate them about the meaning behind each festival. They'd make clay statues of the Hindu Gods, learn how to make certain Indian sweets, and hear stories from the *Mahabharata* (an important Sanskrit epic poem from ancient India). "It was a really happy time in my life," revealed Sonya, the joy evident in her voice. "I loved how carefree I could be."

But middle school and San Jose did not offer the same joys, unfortunately. And as she entered high school, her situation only got worse.

THE LONELINESS BUILDS

"When my parents separated, it was a difficult time for me."

At the very end of eighth grade, Sonya's parents officially filed for a divorce. While her parents never shared a loving relationship and Sonya wasn't close to her father, it was still jarring to no longer have him around the house. Her mother had gained full custody of her, leaving the mother-and-daughter duo to rely on each other even more. "I felt like I had to be strong for her," she said. "Although we became very close, I felt like there were certain things I couldn't talk to her about. I just didn't want to burden her."

Normally, Sonya would turn to her friends to talk about how she was feeling. However, that wasn't quite possible. Shortly after the divorce, she and her mother moved to a newly developing town, nearly eight hours away from San Jose. As a result, she had lost touch with many of her old friends. The few she did remain in contact with did not want to speak on anything more than school or applying for college (which is unsurprising, considering her old friends were now in high school, enveloped in a hypercompetitive, high-pressure academic environment). And since it was still the summer before high school, she hadn't had the opportunity to make any new friends. "I already started feeling isolated in the latter half of middle school," Sonya reflected, "so that move and divorce only made it so much worse."

Anger from the divorce, sadness from not having any cultural connections, loneliness from the move. It was all too much, with little for her to turn to. "I was overwhelmed by my feelings, and I had nowhere to turn to."

And so, Sonya looked to food.

BEGINNINGS OF BED

"It wasn't until ninth grade," Sonya's voice trembled, "that my eating disorder developed."

Naturally, food always had an important role in Sonya's life. Growing up, it was her way to connect with her culture and herself. Food allowed her to show love and feel loved. When the twisty words of her mother tongue, Telugu, fell apart in her mouth, food was what helped maintain the bond with her relatives. And in her current situation (parents separated, mother working, new town, relatives in India, old friends busy), food was the one thing she could rely on. Food allowed her to *feel* again.

"For me," Sonya said, "I always combined my emotions with food. If I was happy, I would eat. If I was sad, I would eat. If I was mad, I would eat. Every emotion reflected on food." Rather than going to her mother or turning to the friends she had, Sonya would instead make her way to the kitchen or the nearest restaurant to process her emotions. At first, it helped her feel better; the buttery taste of pizza or the crunch of salad would allow her to escape from the moment's worries. This method allowed her to not burden her mom or her friends or her relatives with her problems; she felt like she was finally dealing with them on her own.

But over time, it turned into a vicious cycle of elation followed by guilt. The minute Sonya felt an inkling of some emotion, she would consume a meal in response. Once an empty plate reflected back at her, however, her mood deflated, as waves of shame and guilt overcame her—which only led to further consumption of food, to offset these negative feelings. "From that point on," Sonya told me, "I started inching my way closer to rock bottom."

Before long, Sonya's freshman year at her new school began. While she had made a few friends, she found it difficult to confide in them. It was almost like a habit now—to turn to food, rather than the people around her, to process her emotions. It became an almost uncontrollable urge. "I defined everything with what I ate," she said. "Whenever I wanted to feel good or have fun, I would text my friends, "*Oh let's go to this burrito place.*" If I was sad, I would ask if we could go to McDonald's."

Much of what Sonya was experiencing is typical of binge eating disorder. Binge eating disorder (or BED for short) is a type of eating disorder characterized by out-of-control eating. Eating disorders, while not widely understood as part of the world of mental illness, are considered a class of mental health disorders according to the DSM-V. Bulimia, anorexia, binge eating disorder—all of them are often a result of poor mental health, body image, or an inability to manage one's thoughts and/or emotions. While it can develop at any age, it is common for it to start in a person's late teens. Oftentimes, those with BED will eat unusually large amounts of food in a specific amount of time, even when not hungry. Sometimes, they'll even eat in secret, as they feel ashamed or guilty about their eating episodes. Moreover, those with BED generally don't "compensate" for these extra calories (e.g., people with bulimia purging after eating or excessively exercising/dieting the next day). As a result, many with BED are overweight or obese; however, this isn't always the case (Hubbard, n.d.).

That said, it is important to note that binge eating disorder doesn't refer to the occasional consumption of food beyond one's limit, such as on Thanksgiving or on a holiday. Rather, those with BED experience binge episodes at least once a week, eating until they're uncomfortably full or because they feel compelled to (despite not feeling hungry). According to the National Eating Disorder Association (n.d.), the triggers for these episodes can range from stress and poor self-image to boredom or self-doubt. Furthermore, the binge episodes can also result in symptoms of depression, low self-esteem, and feelings of distress or guilt regarding their eating behaviors. In terms of physical health, those with BED are more likely to develop high blood pressure, high cholesterol levels, heart disease, fatigue, joint pain, and type 2 diabetes.

For Sonya, as a result of the frequent weekly binge episodes over the course of two years, BED led to not only psychological effects, but also physical consequences. "Because of how much I ate, because of the turmoil of the emotions I was feeling, I gained a lot of weight. It was the lowest point of my life, both physically and mentally." Standing at 5'1" and 170 pounds, she didn't recognize who she was anymore. At fifteen years old, toward the end of tenth grade, a visit to the doctor informed Sonya she was categorized as "obese." She was now at risk for high cholesterol (due to her oil-laden diet) and type 2 diabetes.

"It was a wake-up call for me," said Sonya. Until now, she felt like she had lost control of her life, as if her actions were not her own. She had consumed food, without taking care of her body. Even though her high school life was balanced—filled with friends and school events—she was always riddled with anxiety and guilt over her binge eating. "After that visit, I no longer wanted to feel that way."

The question was just, how?

IDENTIFYING TRIGGERS AND OBSERVING PATTERNS

"Even though I recognized I wanted to change and get better, I didn't know what I could do or who I could reach out to," Sonya said to me. "I mean, I wasn't even officially diagnosed with binge eating disorder. Only through a bit of internet research did I understand what I was going through." Sonya didn't feel comfortable going to her physician just yet, nor was she willing to openly tell her mother that she had a binge eating disorder. Much less, she didn't even know how to begin the recovery process.

That's when she decided she was better off starting on her own rather than not at all. She began by visiting various websites and blogs of individuals recovering from BED, drawing her plan of action from their words. "I started almost 'cold turkey,'" she said. "I simply tried to *not* eat excessively." Sonya gave a light laugh. "You can imagine how *that* turned out."

While it was a good start toward full recovery (as she had finally recognized she needed the help), Sonya quickly realized it wasn't enough. Simply trying to force herself to eat less and resist her binge episodes wasn't working; she kept falling to the uncontrollable temptations within a week's time. She needed to look deeper, understand what these triggers were—only then could she stop these episodes at the source. "So," revealed Sonya, "I kept a journal that recorded *why* I felt a sudden urge to eat. I would record what happened prior to the binge episode, how I felt during the episode, and what happened after."

It was definitely difficult, at first. To keep a journal tracking each binge, which was often accompanied by feelings of deep shame and guilt, only magnified those feelings. "It was like staring at all my failures." Sometimes, in looking back at all her episodes, she would only spiral into another binge episode. "However, over time, I started seeing a pattern." Finally, Sonya started understanding that her episodes were tied to her emotions. Happy? She would eat. Sad? She would eat. Bored? She would eat. Instead of simply processing or experiencing these emotions, she would turn to food. "That's when it hit me. For me to bring myself out of these binge episodes, I needed to find an outlet for these emotions I was feeling. An outlet that had nothing to do with food."

And that outlet ended up being her best friend.

FINDING SUPPORT IN FRIENDS

By the end of tenth grade, Sonya had managed to surround herself with a trustworthy group of friends, finally feeling more settled in since moving two years ago. Although she still struggled with being vulnerable with others, Sonya always made sure to be there for everyone else. People came to her whenever they needed help or just a shoulder to cry on. Her kind brown eyes and warm demeanor made her seem trustworthy; people couldn't help but be comforted by her presence.

The only issue was that no one played that role for her, up until this point.

While she didn't mind others entrusting her with their deepest feelings, Sonya kept others at arm's length when it came to her own emotions. "A lot of people simply thought I was a 'go-with-the-flow' type of person," she said. "Since I never really talked about how I really felt, everyone just assumed I was alright with anything. No one thought I was struggling."

But Sonya *was* struggling. And she needed help.

"I read how one of the best ways to process your emotions was to talk about them with others," she recalled, "but I didn't want to go to my mom." So, she decided to turn to one of her closest friends from school, Rachel. "We always did everything together," Sonya said animatedly, laughing. "We went to games together, did homework together, gossiped about boys together." Suddenly, her voice dropped, her mouth lifting into a small smile. "Even though I never really talked about my feelings with Rachel, she was the only one that came to mind. She was always sweet, looking out for me. Plus, we were really close." Sonya paused for a second. "It seemed like the obvious choice, really."

The first time was hard. "I felt awkward!" Sonya exclaimed. Though Rachel was likely surprised, she didn't hesitate to become that emotional support for Sonya. "Rachel made me feel comfortable. I never felt judged for what I was feeling or what I was going through; she just supported me." By opening up to Rachel, Sonya unlocked a whole host of support from her friend. Now, when she felt upset or an urge to eat without reason, she knew she could just call or text Rachel to help redirect her thinking or process her emotions.

"It revolutionized my relationship with food," Sonya said. "I didn't turn to it for comfort or to celebrate; I simply had to go to my friends." She was no longer overwhelmed by her emotions, as she had an outlet (Rachel) to help her experience, process, and understand what she felt. This alone assisted Sonya in her journey to recovery; in managing her emotions, she was able to greatly reduce the number of binge episodes she had. The presence of sadness, happiness, anxiousness, anger, etc. no longer automatically triggered an uncontrollable urge to eat.

She had control, once again. It was clear that the support system she was starting to build was aiding in her mental wellness.

FINDING SUPPORT IN FAMILY

With her emotions slightly more in check, Sonya felt confident enough to start working toward a healthier her. "What led me to address my eating disorder in the first place was how it was threatening my physical and mental health." Though her binge episodes had now greatly reduced, Sonya still retained the extra weight. "Not only did it make me not *feel* good, I was also worried by the possibility of developing various health conditions if I didn't adopt a healthier lifestyle." While she could always exercise, she knew diet would also be a key part of her recovery process. However, her diet was essentially dictated by her mom. "I ate whatever my mom cooked," Sonya said. "And she cooked the richest, most delicious Indian food—which was exactly the source of the problem with my diet."

While Indian dishes vary by region and are often quite healthy (with the wide expanse of vegetables and meat they include), they are often united by a love for oil and frying, salt, and sweets. These are fine in moderation but can quickly cause negative health effects if high amounts are consumed daily. However, Sonya didn't want to completely eradicate Indian cuisine from her diet. "I didn't want to lose my connection to my culture," she said. On one hand, her current diet consisted of many unhealthy staples; on the other, she didn't want to give up these staples as they were reflections of her cultural background. "I was stuck on what to do."

There was only one place she could turn to resolve this dilemma of hers: her mom. "It was kind of scary," Sonya recalled, reflecting. "I mean, my mom is my number one supporter, but opening up to my mother about how I was struggling and needed her help...that was terrifying to me. I never really had done that before."

But Sonya knew she had no other choice and needed her mom's help. So, one random afternoon after school, she marched up to her mom in the kitchen and declared she wanted to become healthier. She explained how she had been trying to cut down her consumption but wanted to take bigger steps to change her lifestyle. "[However], I couldn't quite bring myself to tell her that I had a binge eating disorder," Sonya said, "so she just saw it as me wanting to become healthy and lose weight." But it ultimately didn't matter, as Sonya had her mom's full support—and her mom was determined to provide healthy alternatives to the Indian dishes Sonya loved.

Instead of carb-loaded white rice, her mom prepared *roti* and brown rice. Instead of making curry in tablespoons of oil, her mom would use small amounts of olive oil or coconut oil.

Sweets were limited to special occasions, while evening walks became a daily occurrence. Over the course of a year, she and her mom—and later, her grandfather when they visited India—adopted various small changes to transform their lifestyle into one that supported Sonya's goal to become healthier. As a result of her mother's support, not only was Sonya seeing obvious health improvements, but she also noticed that her mental health started improving, too. "My head was once filled with constant anxious thoughts, hatred towards myself and my body, and feelings of despair," she explained. "But as the months and years went by, I started seeing less and less of that." As exemplified by Sonya, physical and mental health are closely tied; one can have a profound effect on the other. So, when she started taking care of her body—after addressing the root cause of her eating disorder habits—her mind became a better place, as well.

Needless to say, it was a welcome change.

REFLECTING ON THE JOURNEY THUS FAR

Today, at seventeen years old, Sonya stands as an integral member of her community, bright and chatty. No longer isolated due to hypercompetitive communities, Sonya is now heavily involved with numerous local cultural organizations. From helping to plan neighborhood events for various Hindu festivals to organizing community drives, Sonya has finally found her connection to her culture once again.

Moreover, her binge episodes have become rare, as she works with her mom and friends to transform into a healthier version of herself. "It was never about weight loss for me." Rather, it was about adopting healthy habits, both mentally and physically. From learning to confide in her friends to process her emotions without food to transforming her life into an active and nutritious one with the help of her mom, Sonya knows she couldn't have gotten to this place of recovery on her own. Through the support of her family and friends, who constantly encouraged her, helped her, and believed in her, did she get better—both mentally and physically. She is no longer bound by her eating disorder/habits, all thanks to the support system she created.

Sonya may have not utilized professional services to get to this point, but she didn't do this alone either. In choosing to trust in others, asking for their help, and looking to their support, she was able to take the steps toward mental wellness and recovery.

"My friends and family were essential to my recovery and the improvement of my mental and physical health," Sonya emphasized to me. "And for that, I will always be grateful to them."

THE BREAKTHROUGH BOX

Mental illness is not meant to be endured alone. Just like how it takes a village to raise a child, it takes a team to reach and maintain mental wellness. So, don't hesitate to reach out to your friends and find your support. It just may make your days a little bit easier.

And to those who have friends suddenly reaching out to them—you never know where somebody else is at, so listen without assumption. They're taking a brave step in opening up to you, so honor their vulnerability and strength with non-judgmental support.

PART 3

PARENTS ARE ALLIES (AND WHY SOMETIMES THEY'RE NOT)

For many, it is effortless to communicate with friends rather than family.

Friends, often of the same generation, tend to be easier to connect with, since they seem to sympathize and relate. They generally share the same values, graced with the perspectives and knowledge that allow us to not feel judged and quite safe. Parents, on the other hand, are often a different story. The fear of judgment, the fear of disappointment, the possibility of being dismissed—all of these make it difficult to open up to them.

Especially for many individuals of Asian background, the stigmatization of and blatant disregard toward mental illness and mental health makes it even harder. After all, in many Asian cultures, mental illness is seen as something that only afflicts the "mentally weak." When living in the United States, the land of freedom and opportunity, many parents believe there is no reason for their children to be sad (depression) or anxious (anxiety)—only those who've undergone tremendous hardship and trauma are considered to have a "rightful reason" for their mental illness. Anything otherwise is merely an excuse, a result of being too pampered, something that doesn't exist.

Thus, with this attitude prevalent in many communities, most become unsure if their parents will believe them. They're doubtful that their parents will understand or will even *want* to understand. They're not sure if they'll be connected to resources or if they'll just be told to "suck it up" and endure. So, many never tell, silently struggling with no end in sight. We just assume there is no point; we assume there is no way for us to make our parents understand.

That's what Mirabelle Lei and Tyson thought, too, after years of struggling with their mental health. Initially, it was something Lei and Tyson deemed impossible—after all, their cultural background and upbringing made it obvious that conversations around mental health weren't welcome in the family. However, as the two quickly realized, sometimes there are reasons behind this inability to understand and talk about mental health. In some cases, as with Tyson, these reasons will always prevent our parents from being someone we can turn to. But in other cases, like with Lei, if we show compassion to our parents, patiently breaking down the walls and expectations they have, we may unlock a new normal—one where mental health is discussed, where support is given.

Ultimately, Mirabelle Lei's and Tyson's stories help us understand our parents and their role in our mental health journeys. They make us rethink the way we view AAPI parents.

Parents may seem indifferent to our struggles, *but have we considered why?* We may think it is impossible for them to understand, *but how would we know if we don't try?*

CHAPTER 7

MIRABELLE LEI

———

Her eyes. Everyone always noticed her eyes.

Her brown irises were always framed by thick black liner, which tapered off into a razor-sharp edge. Her hair was never one color for too long: bubblegum pink, orchid purple, baby blue. Like a chameleon, she was always changing her look, matching it to her ever-evolving moods. Her eyes, however, were the one constant.

Today, I was greeted by brunette hair, the tips of which were bleached blonde. Her ears were decorated with an assortment of earrings, while her dark, torn jeans were held snug against her waist with a metallic chain. A black graphic tee completed the outfit, tucked loosely into the waistband of her jeans. Taking her laptop, she splayed herself across her bedroom floor, angling the camera toward her face. She laid flat, her chin resting against her palm, as her legs swung up in the air. She watched me quietly, waiting.

At nineteen years old, Mirabelle Lei was the epitome of an independent thinker. Growing up in a strict Asian household that upheld deep Christian values, *who* Lei was to become seemed to be predetermined, and for the longest time, Lei herself believed that was who she was going to be:

pious, God-fearing, conservative with her values and beliefs. Although these traits are never bad to have, they weren't quite her truth. "I decided that I would define what I found to be important, discover what *I* wanted out of life," Lei remarked, her voice unwavering.

And that was exactly what she did and still continues to do.

Currently pursuing a degree in journalism at a university located in Southern California, Lei has committed herself to learning about society through experimentation and observation. From her sexuality to her academic interests to her extracurricular passions, she refuses to be confined by her parents' expectations or community's judgments. By day, she immerses herself in words, learning how to wield their power to communicate the truths of our world. By night, she roams the streets (or rather, in the age of COVID-19, the internet) to sample new tastes and discover new sounds. Her weekdays are spent with a book in hand, nose nearly touching the pages, as she searches for the answers to the world's problems. The weekend brings a host of new faces, each individual providing a unique story for her to keep tucked into her heart and mind.

No matter what the situation brought, Lei embraced every moment with a fearless heart. However, that courage to explore and defy expectations was not her only remarkable quality.

There was a sense of kindness in the way she spoke and the manner in which she moved. Her eyes would stay trained on yours, as a way of telling you that what you said mattered. She would laugh at all the right moments, quick to compliment your sense of humor—and your hair. She wouldn't leave without mentioning how beautiful (or handsome) you were, making sure to send a follow-up text of how much fun she had with you. When one was with Lei, they felt safe, wanted, beautiful. Although, after a lifetime of hating oneself, that kindness towards others was only to be expected.

INSECURITIES IN IOWA

Mirabelle Lei's story begins with that of her parents.

Since the Immigration Act of 1965, the United States experienced another influx of Asian immigrants, including those hailing from Korea. Lei's parents and grandparents were part of this third wave of Korean migration, fleeing from a military dictatorship that presented both political and economic insecurity (Min, 2011). "Although my father was Chinese, both my parents grew up in Korea," she recounted. During the early 1980s, when they were only adolescents, Lei's parents made the three-week maritime trek with their respective families, ultimately arriving in the dry cornfields of Iowa. It wasn't until the 1990s, when her parents arrived at college, that the pair met. After completing their bachelor's degrees, the two quickly married, producing Lei in 2001 and her brother a couple of years later.

"I was born in Iowa," Lei said, with a wry laugh. "Although," she quickly added, "I was only there for a few years." Despite living in a state that had historically welcomed East Asian immigrants (Monsoon Asians and Pacific Islanders in Solidarity, n.d.), Lei found very few people who looked like her. From her community members to her classmates to the magazines on the shelves of her local grocery store, Lei's life was defined by her white counterparts. "When I was in elementary school, there were only two Korean kids in my entire school," she said. "And I was one of them." The lack of representation—and sense of community in relation to her identity as a Korean-Chinese—led to a feeling of "otherness" within her. She found it difficult to connect with others, beginning to view her ethnic features as something to be ashamed of rather than celebrated.

It was only compounded by her peers, who would take every opportunity to point out those differences. "In elementary, it was more of an innocent observation, a curious remark," Lei said. "Kids would stick their fingers in my face, asking why my nose was so wide and my eyes so small." With teachers not bothering to put an end to this behavior—nor teaching about the fine line between curiosity and cultural insensitivity—she started to associate her physical features as the source of her problems; they seemed to be the reason why she never truly belonged. "I know they never had any malicious intent—I mean, we were all so young—but it still affected the way I viewed myself." Lei's mouth turned down, her shoulder sinking ever so slightly. "The only thing I wanted to be was white."

EUROCENTRISM AND BODY IMAGE

It's a statement that is uttered by far too many young children and adolescents alike: the desire to be white. As discussed in a study by Mr. Sheeba Saghir and Dr. Lynda Hyland (2017), body image is a "multidimensional construct, comprising of feelings, thoughts, and perceptions that individuals hold toward their body." This "image" is easily influenced by an individual's surroundings, including by what the media presents as the "desirable" body type and facial features. Who we see on the screen, who we see in affluent roles and positions of power, the daily interaction we have with our communities—all of that plays a role in what we consider the "ideal" (Saghir and Hyland, 2017).

For many BIPOC (Black, Indigenous, and people of color), that "ideal" becomes their white counterparts. After experiencing and watching society's blatant preference for their white peers, colleagues, and friends, it becomes difficult for BIPOC to eradicate the feeling that they might be *less*. Time and time again, those who possess Eurocentric features (think: fair skin, narrow nose, more "delicate" lips, slimmer face, etc.) continue to receive promotions, job opportunities, and social acceptance; even at an early age, nonwhite children are exposed to adults who dote on their whiter friends (Stepanova and Strube, 2012). All of these experiences and interactions culminate into a deep feeling of inadequacy within their own skin, contributing to a lower self-esteem and severe dissatisfaction with their body image. Individuals—including those of Asian descent—begin to feel their lives would be much better, if only they were *white*. They start to believe there's something wrong with them—that they're ugly and unworthy—*just because they aren't white*.

"While much conversation centers around how the experiences of marginalized communities are tainted by the institutions that serve the white majority," relates Dr. Reddy from our interview, "we fail to look at how these very same institutions have certain psychological effects. Quite literally, our identities can lead to mental health struggles." From undertaking potentially harmful procedures (like skin bleaching, a practice that lightens areas of darker skin via harsh chemicals, and iris implants) to spiraling among harsh self-critiques (leading to eating disorders and body dysmorphia), BIPOC individuals have been deeply impacted by the inherent biases of society. It's an unfortunate reality that is creating long-lasting negative effects on the mental health of minorities in the United States. Children and young adults start to create a different type of hatred toward themselves: a hatred based on their ethnicity, an identity they can never change. Left unaddressed, it becomes a duality that causes a lifetime of suffering.

For Mirabelle Lei, that's a reality she knows all too well.

INTERNALIZED RACISM: A RISK FACTOR TO BDD

Lei's early childhood experiences with her community members (like for many BIPOC children in the United States) left a sour taste in her mouth—and her mind. It started as an alienating feeling, as she noticed she did not (and would not) look like her white peers—and would never experience the same privileges they did. "They [the white community] were my everything," Lei told me. "I started to compare myself to them. My sense of worth came from how much I looked, talked, and acted like them." In middle school, however, it quickly morphed into an intense hatred of the very features that made her Korean-Chinese.

"At age eleven, my family and I moved to California," she said. "But not the California everyone else knows." In contrast to the glitz and glamor of Los Angeles, Lei moved to Atwater. Located within the Central Valley, Atwater was in the center of the agricultural area of California. As a rural town, dominated by migrant Hispanic workers and white people, Atwater lacked resources, diversity, and cultural understanding. Rather than the sense of belonging she was hoping to find, Lei found a community filled with hostility and disgust toward her culture and her identity. Anything that marked her as Asian, and thus different, only made her a bigger target among her peers.

"I would bring *Kimbap*, a Korean sushi roll, for lunch," she recounted. "And the first thing they'd do is hold their noses, asking what was that 'ugly thing.' They'd spend all of lunch taunting me, saying how gross my culture was." But the food wasn't the only thing they would bully her for. From her physical features to the way she pronounced certain words, Lei's peers instilled a deep self-hatred within her. "Anything that made me Asian, I hated," she said. "I hated my hair, I hated my wide nose, I hated my eyes…I hated every aspect of my body that connected me to my identity and culture."

Although she was never officially diagnosed, the thoughts and symptoms Lei was experiencing matched many of the typical signs of Body Dysmorphic Disorder (BDD). As defined by the Mayo Clinic Staff (2019), BDD is a mental health disorder characterized by an inability to stop thinking about the "one or more perceived defects or flaws" in one's appearance. While the causes of BDD aren't exactly known, researchers have found that there are certain factors that can increase the likelihood of developing BDD. These factors include low self-esteem, critical peers or parents, pressures from a society that equates certain physical appearances with beauty and value, traumatic events, and childhood emotional conflicts (Cleveland Clinic, 2020). In Lei's case, it was likely a combination of these factors.

"Growing up in Iowa, then Atwater, the world didn't contain people who resembled me." From childhood peers who bullied and alienated her to a society that valued Eurocentric features, Lei's life experiences showed her that there wasn't value in *who* she was because of the *way* she looked (i.e., not white). It impacted her mental health and how she viewed herself, developing into an intense self-hatred of her appearance and creating an unending stream of negative, self-critical thoughts.

Oftentimes, these thoughts become all-consuming, causing a variety of obsessive behaviors: repeatedly checking the mirror to scrutinize the feature(s) in question, grooming constantly, seeking reassurance from others, and frequently comparing one's appearance with others. These behaviors aren't periodic; rather, they are continuous, sometimes even taking up hours of one's day, causing severe (emotional) distress and disruptions in daily life (Cleveland Clinic, 2020). For Lei, sometimes she would spend nearly the entire weekend fixated on her face and features. "I would spend hours in front of the mirror, hating what I saw," she said. "It was like there was a voice in the back of my mind, constantly reminding me of how ugly I was, how I would never be pretty like the white people around me." At a moment's notice, her mind would be consumed by these hateful voices—voices that sounded eerily like her middle school peers.

Left untreated, body dysmorphic disorder can even develop into further mental health issues—which was exactly what happened with Lei.

THE DESCENT INTO DEPRESSION

"My family never spoke about mental health and mental illness," Lei said. "So, I never really thought what I was experiencing was related to my mental health. I didn't think it warranted a visit to a therapist or any sort of help like that." Many individuals experiencing BDD often have the same line of thinking; not being told any different, they view their thoughts as normal, as something that isn't part of the world of mental health. Thus, very few seek out help, until it morphs into more severe symptoms, such as an eating disorder, anxiety, or, in Lei's case, a mood disorder (Cleveland Clinic, 2020).

"I started experiencing depressive episodes and thoughts," she said. "I would find myself coming home, unwilling to hang out with friends or interact with my family. I'd be in my room, disconnected from the world, crying. Sometimes, even just being in the classroom was too much, at this point." Easily drained, Lei didn't have much energy for anything. No longer was she interested in pursuing her hobbies and passions; instead, she spent her time mindlessly scrolling through various social media platforms. On the rare occasions she had the motivation to, Lei would pour her depressive thoughts into her journal. Most days, however, she'd lay on her bed, unmoving, dreading the next day and the days after that. Isolation and separation became her answer to everything.

"It was partly my body dysmorphia and partly the depressive episodes I was having," Lei reflected. "I didn't want to go anywhere, do anything. The thought of being out in public... it was just the last place I wanted to be." All of this took a slow mental toll on her, as the never-ending self-critiques and depressive behaviors transformed into a constant heavy and negative feeling in her mind.

But just when she thought it couldn't get any worse, it did. After a shocking revelation, her mental health only further deteriorated, taking a turn for the worse.

A SHOCKING REVELATION

Born into an intensely religious Christian household, Lei's childhood was defined by her parent's conservative Christian values. Sunday morning would be dedicated to church, while Thursday evenings she would find herself surrounded by fellow youth Christians for Bible study. Everyone held the same values, believed in the same ideals, and lived by the same principles—including her friends and peers. In Iowa, there was little room to question the morals that guided her family, as many of her fellow community members shared the same ones. In California, however, that started to change. Lei began to develop her own world views, which differed greatly from her parent's. That development did not come quickly or easily—rather it was initiated by her brother. More specifically, it stemmed from her brother's sexual identity.

The summer prior to her freshman year of high school, Lei and her family moved to Dublin, California. Located in the Bay Area, Dublin was a suburban haven, complete with a sizable Asian demographic. Although Dublin wasn't necessarily ethnically diverse, as the town was populated with a majority of white and Asian residents, it was a pleasant change in environment for Lei. "There were more people who looked like me," Lei said. "And for a while, it felt nice." Although she was still experiencing a constant stream of critiquing thoughts and bouts of depression, she felt less isolated and alienated. She felt an inherent sense of community and comfort in knowing that there were people who looked like her. That feeling of relative peace and contentment, however, did not last long.

Just a couple of months into her freshman year, she started noticing her younger brother's "odd" behavior. He would spend a lot of time on his phone, a sappy smile on his face. Was it a girl?

"That was my first thought," Lei revealed. "But I wasn't the only one who noticed his sudden change in behavior." Lei's mother became curious about what was making her son act so lovesick. So, in an attempt to discover the truth, Mrs. Lei went through her son's phone, only to discover the farthest thing from a girlfriend: a boyfriend.

"My mom just freaked." Lei's family was brought up believing homosexuality was a sin. So, it was not surprising that her mother's reaction was not a positive one. "She immediately started trying to 'fix' him," Lei said. "It was like her worst nightmare had come true, especially since our Church and our community did not accept the gay community." From having numerous talks with her brother to bringing him to the priest, Lei's mother tried her hardest to suppress his "gay desires." Even Lei herself was initially shocked by her brother's truth. "I just didn't know how to react," she said. "A part of me was really bothered—the other part of me was extremely concerned. I thought he was now going to go to hell." Her voice dropped, her face suddenly shameful and filled with regret. "And I took every chance back then to remind him of that," she whispered, her voice strained.

In response to the family's reaction, Lei's brother shut down. "He entered a really bad place," she said. He began to distance himself away from not only his family members, but also his friends. He'd spend his time in his room, keeping his blinds closed and losing interest in his regular daily activities. By this point, he had cut things off with his boyfriend, in fear that his boyfriend too would be exposed to his family members (who weren't aware of their son's sexual identity either). Over time, his appetite decreased, causing him to lose weight until he was nearly just skin and bones. Lei could do nothing but watch as her brother wasted away, caught in what seemed to her to be his depression.

ADDRESSING MENTAL HEALTH IN LGBTQIA+ YOUTH

Due to the peer, familial, and societal rejections they can face, LGBTQ+ youth are at an increased risk of developing or experiencing mental health disorders. In fact, LGBTQ individuals are more than twice as likely to have a mental health disorder in their lifetime, compared to heterosexual men and women (American Psychiatric Association Division of Diversity and Health Equity, 2017). They're also more likely to seriously contemplate and attempt suicide, compared to their heterosexual, cisgender peers (The Trevor Project, 2020). As concluded in a research study by Dr. Megan Sutter and Dr. Paul Perrin (2016), LGBTQ-based discrimination has an effect on "suicidal ideation through mental health" on LGBTQ youth.

While these figures are already concerning, additional identities—like race and ethnicity—can also impact the mental health of LGBTQ youth. When it comes to Asian/Pacific Islander LGBTQ youth, although they were reported as having lower rates of depression and suicide ideation, they were less likely to come out to their parents about their sexuality, in fear of retaliation and rejection. Family acceptance, or rather the lack thereof, is a factor that impacts the risk of suicidal ideation and self-harm (The Trevor Project, 2016). Coupled with the wider cultural rejection of (and discrimination toward) the LGBTQ community, API communities are quite literally harming their LGBTQ children. A research study by Dr. Ching (2018), a clinical psychologist and postdoctoral associate at the Yale School of Medicine, summarizes it best: the structural oppressions, interpersonal discrimination, internalized minority stress cognitions, maladaptive coping, and poor social support all contribute to the negative mental health outcomes in LGBTQ Asian Americans. API

LGBTQ youth are faced with a variety of stressors and factors that increase their likelihood of developing mental health problems, while decreasing their likelihood to seek proper treatment and help (Ching et al., 2018).

In Lei's family, the lack of acceptance was contributing to the development and severity of her brother's mental health issue. "My younger brother was a vibrant individual," Lei said. "So, to see his light suddenly dim was devastating—but I was still reeling from the news about his sexual identity. I didn't know what to believe." That lack of certainty not only affected her brother's mental health, but also her own.

HITTING ROCK BOTTOM—AND FIGHTING TO COME BACK UP

With her brother in the throes of depression, Lei's precarious mental health situation slipped down to its lowest point. "It was one thing on top of another," she said. "Everywhere I looked, I seemed to be staring into a gaping black hole. And I didn't have anywhere to go to. I was in a very dark place, and I couldn't do anything." By now, the voices in the back of her mind had transformed into a monster that was always perched on her shoulder, whispering how she was "worthless," "disgusting to look at," a "terrible sister" and "even worse daughter." Her heart was drenched with feelings of hopelessness and pessimism; her mind was a prison, trapping her in an endless cycle of demotivation and self-doubt.

And she couldn't take it anymore.

Initially, Lei attempted to seek out help of some sort by reaching out to her school counselors. Partly bothered by her recent discovery of her brother's homosexuality and partly struggling with her general mental health, she decided to take a leap of faith and reach out to her counselors.

"It wasn't very helpful if I'm being honest," Lei said. Although she was careful not to describe her body-obsessive thoughts, Lei did reveal the constant "worrying" and how she'd just feel "down." The school counselors, in response, would simply try to redirect her to professional therapists, citing how they could help. "Looking back," she said, pursing her lips thoughtfully. "I understand they were trying to get me to seek out help, but at that point, I wasn't ready. I didn't want my parents to know I needed help—I didn't even want to admit I needed professional help." The school counselors didn't understand this, though. Lacking the cultural sensitivity and knowledge, they would repeatedly try to get Lei to seek professional help, to no avail. In the end, rather than showing how she could utilize the resources around her (like online therapy groups, mindful thinking, etc.), the counselors would simply allow her to stay in their offices until she felt ready to go back. "Even though they didn't *help* me, per se," Lei explained. "It was still a place for me to go to when I couldn't handle being at school."

With a school filled with white professionals that didn't quite understand, friends seemed to be the next logical place to go to. But Lei didn't utilize that space. "I felt guilty," she said. "I didn't want to burden them, when they might have been going through worse." With friends no longer a possibility, that left only one place to go: *home*. Unfortunately, that wasn't a viable option for her—at least, not at first.

THE (PARENTAL) BARRIER

Parenting styles have an effect on whether or not a child is willing and ready to open up. In the Lei family household, bad days had repercussions; a tone that was a bit too rude or a voice that was a bit too loud was met with swift consequences.

This disciplinary home environment ultimately led to no real outlet for Lei or her sibling; they couldn't—and wouldn't—go to their parents, as they learned that to speak out about one's frustrations wasn't tolerated.

"That's where the issue lies," Dr. Paige Lee, a clinical psychologist at UC Berkeley states. "It [emotions or mental health] is never talked about in these households." The reason for this lack of conversation lies in one simple fact: it's never been modeled for kids, nor their parents. Many cultures and families within the Asian community don't model a behavior where they're open to conversing about mental health, emotions, or mental well-being. Instead, as Dr. Lee explains, the "suck it up and endure" mentality is modeled—and enforced— by many Asian families.

That left Lei in a difficult spot. On one hand, she had parents who didn't understand the value of empathy and resources to better one's mental health. On the other, Lei herself didn't understand how to reach out to them.

"Honestly, I think I would've allowed myself to wallow in my depressive state and body dysmorphia," she said. "But because my brother was struggling too, I knew I had to do something." By now, about a year later, she had come to terms with her brother's sexuality; it had taken months of wrestling with the principles promoted by her faith and her brother's reality, but she had eventually come to her own conclusion— that being part of the LGBTQ community did not make someone *bad* or deserving of rejection. "That realization was my first leap into uncharted territory," Lei said. "It was the first time I had actually thought and decided for myself."

Although she had unlocked a newfound sense of independence, this didn't change how her family viewed and treated mental health. Lei knew her brother needed help; she knew *she* needed help—and her parents were the only way she and her brother were going to get it. It would require not only a conversation with her parents, but also a sense of understanding and acceptance about mental health.

As Lei thought about all of this, there was only one word jumping around in her mind. *How?*

THE TURNING POINT

"When I think back to that day," Lei said. "I can't help but feel lucky. It had to be pure, dumb luck I caught her right at that moment."

When Lei was in her junior year of high school, she had managed to muster up the motivation and the energy to be a part of her school's journalism club. The week of the release of their monthly publication, the club would require its members to stay late, in order to review all submissions and ensure everything was set for print. That meant on the second Tuesday of every month, she didn't come home until seven in the evening.

This was an occurrence the family had come to expect. A couple of months into her junior year, it was routine. But in April of 2018, the monthly Tuesday meeting was canceled. Due to a family emergency, the editor in chief of the club decided to postpone publication, unwilling to have the rest of the team handle that month's publication. Being a last-minute cancellation, Lei didn't have the opportunity to inform her parents that she would be home earlier that Tuesday. She merely made her way back home, her mind filled with the melancholic tunes playing through her headphones, expecting to find an empty house.

What she found instead, as she entered her home and made her way past the living room, was her mother. Her mother curled up on the kitchen floor, crying. Her mother, whose body shook with silent sobs, clutching at her now-graying hair. Her mother, the woman who never betrayed an ounce of emotion, with tears streaming down her wrinkled cheeks, staining her pale-yellow shirt. Her mother, who didn't believe in mental health, having a mental breakdown of her own.

"I was shocked," said Lei. "For a moment, I just stood there, taking her in. That was the first time I ever saw my mother in such a vulnerable state—it was the first time I realized that my mom was human, too. That she experienced emotions and stressors and struggled with her mental health like the rest of us."

Quickly, Lei leapt into action.

She dropped her backpack on the floor, then gingerly made her way to her mother. "I didn't want to spook her or anything. So, I quietly announced that I was there, then put my hand on her back." When her mother didn't pull away, she started rubbing her back soothingly. Slowly, the tears resided, replaced with deep, calming breaths. Finally, after what had been about fifteen minutes, Lei's mother raised her head, looking at her, a look of shame in her eyes. "That remains to be one of the most heartbreaking moments of my life," Lei said. "My mom was *ashamed* just because I caught her in a vulnerable state. It's like she felt she had failed as a mother, in that moment. And I hated that."

Realizing her mother needed her, to process whatever she was feeling, Lei asked her mother if she wanted to talk. "To my surprise, she said yes," Lei said. They moved from the kitchen floor to the living room, seated next to each other on their long couch. "I just held her hand and let her talk."

It turned into a two-hour conversation, with Lei's mother opening up to her, expressing the remorse, guilt, and confusion she felt from that moment. They spoke about her stressors, her mental health. And slowly, her mother started feeling mentally better. "When I knew my mother was alright again, I squeezed her hand and stood up, about to go to my room," Lei told me. "But just as I was about to leave, my mother gripped my hand, pulling me back."

At that, Lei turned around, raising her eyebrows at her mom, in question.

Is this how you and your brother always feel? her mother asked.

Caught off guard, she stood there, quiet. "That was the first time my mother had asked about my mental health," Lei said to me. "That was the first time she tried to actually understand."

Wanting to be truthful, Lei answered honestly. "I told her, yes. I told her that was how we felt—and sometimes it felt worse." Jumping on the opportunity, she forged ahead to explain. "I explained how even though we felt that heaviness always, we didn't have to. I spoke to my mom about how there was help, how we could support each other, as a family." In response, her mother gave her a comforting smile, not saying much. Although unsure if she got through to her mother, Lei headed to her room, slightly exhausted from the day's events.

But what Lei didn't know, as she laid down to take a nap that afternoon, was that things were going to change in her household—for the better.

SEEKING MENTAL WELLNESS, AS A FAMILY

"After that day, it was like a switch had flipped in my mom's brain," Lei revealed, with a small, joyful laugh.

Now understanding the emotional and mental turmoil her kids were going through, Lei's mother began putting effort toward addressing her children's mental health. Within months, Lei's parents had invested in a therapy dog for her brother, along with professional therapy services. Although they haven't fully accepted her brother's sexuality, Lei is thankful her parents were at least working to better his mental health. "I know it will take them time to fully accept him, but at least now his mental health is at a better place. And for that, I will always count my blessings." Family time now included checking on each other's well-being, with mental health conversations more common in the house. (The section "Resources for Further Exploration" will include links to some websites that help you and your family have these same conversations.)

As for Lei herself, she began using journaling as a means of changing her thinking, to remind herself of her strength and beauty, and to redirect the negative and critical thoughts of her body dysmorphia. In an effort to improve her overall mental health, her parents also enrolled her in an online therapy group they found through personal research, which has equipped her with the tools and support needed to recover and heal. Over the past two years, journaling, combined with her online therapy groups, has helped Lei immensely to address her BDD, while reducing her depressive thoughts and feelings. Even today, by utilizing her online resources (such as mindfulness videos and deep breathing exercises), she has been able to steadily work towards a better mental health while addressing her mental health issues.

Conversations about mental health and receiving help for a mental health issue weren't normalized behaviors in Lei's family. After all, there was no one to model it. However, after Lei's act of compassion, in which she worked to address her mom's mental state, the behavior was finally modeled for a key member of the family, which then spread to the rest of the household. Though Lei's mother could have chosen to continue ignoring her mental health, as well as her children's, she didn't. Rather, upon reflection, she broke away from what she had been taught, instead embracing practices that recognized the importance of mental health and treatments that would help address any issues. In this way, Lei's mother established a new precedence in the family—one that normalized mental health and taking care of it.

From that one simple act of caring for someone in a mental health episode, and having a conversation about it afterward, Lei ultimately created a family environment more sensitive to the mental health of its inhabitants. This just goes to show how a moment of empathy and understanding can change how an entire family views and talks about mental health. Sometimes, that change comes from those small, but important, moments.

A NEW HOPE FOR THE FUTURE

What had started as body dysmorphia stemming from a community disconnect and childhood bullying became a mental health battle with BDD and depression. It turned into seeking out help from her school—only to not receive the help she truly needed. In the end, through her words and the online world, Lei slowly brought herself out of that low place of depression. By showing compassion, she was able to teach her parents the importance of mental health, creating a home environment more supportive of everyone's mental well-being. Through her resources, she was able to slowly let go of the harmful thoughts and behaviors that accompanied her BDD. By challenging what she has always been told, she gained confidence in her identity and in her ability to discover the world in her own way.

Mirabelle Lei, along with her mother, has ushered in much-needed change to her own life and to the lives of those around her. Her brother has begun to recover, utilizing his therapy dog and the knowledge he gained from his therapy sessions to better navigate his depressive episodes. Though he still struggles at home with the tensions surrounding his sexuality, he was able to find the support—within Lei, his therapist, and his friends—to deal with it all. Her mother now openly speaks about mental health with friends and family alike, even deciding (most recently) to visit a therapist for herself. It's clear that Lei's family is taking large strides toward achieving mental wellness.

In reflecting on her mental health journey from the past nineteen years, Lei recognizes it's an ongoing process. "After wishing you were white, worshiping those who were white, and seeing that you yourself weren't white...that's difficult to get over," she said, her voice quiet but steady. "It's hard to appreciate the features you were given when you spent a lifetime hating it. It's hard to be happy when you spent a lifetime feeling depressed and negative." For a moment, there was nothing but silence. Then, slowly, Lei lifted her head, a small smile on her face. "But I'm learning," she said. "I'm learning to love it all. I'm learning to treat myself kindly, to bring myself out of those lows. I'm learning the value of relying upon and opening up to my parents, of having their support."

She brought her gaze to mine, her almond-shaped eyes still surrounded by that thick, black eyeliner. "But most importantly, I'm learning to *accept* me, mental health struggles and all."

THE BREAKTHROUGH BOX

While it can be a terrifying thought to open up to your parents, as the cultural stigmas are often deeply ingrained in them, you should not discount them from your mental health journey immediately. Rather, despite your fears, it is important to be open and ready to communicate. After all, how can your parents know that you're struggling and need help, if you don't talk to them about what is going on?

And for those with family who are struggling with their mental health—have an open mind and an open heart. While mental health may be a foreign concept, it is still a real aspect that can have large impacts. So, do your best to explore the world of mental health and help that individual seek treatment.

CHAPTER 8

TYSON

———

The stench of alcohol clung to his skin. Hands trembling slightly, he held the green bottle by its neck and brought it to his lips. He tipped his head back, allowing the burning sensation of the liquid to travel down his throat and settle in the pit of his stomach. His teeth were now numb, his gums feeling far too big for his mouth. What day was it? Tuesday? Thursday?

Tyson didn't know. All he knew was this bottle of *Heineken*. He took another long drink, then lazily eyed the clock, reading the time. *8:04 a.m.* It was time for him to go to school. Tyson reluctantly put his bottle down and grabbed his backpack. It sagged from the weight of his textbooks—though he rarely even looked at them these days. He couldn't bear to think, much alone read about some long-gone philosopher or the human body's glycolysis process. All he wanted to do was numb his mind—and the alcohol was allowing him to do just that. Unable to resist, he took one more, quick sip from the *Heineken* bottle before leaving his apartment.

Now, he was ready to go.

For the past three months, Tyson's days tended to follow a very particular schedule: wake up, drink whiskey, wine, or beer in the morning, arrive at school and drift from class to class, go to swim practice barely sober, come home to finish the bare minimum of assignments, then finally fall asleep with yet another bottle in hand. This wasn't how a seventeen-year-old should have been living his life, yet Tyson didn't know any other way to deal with the pain. In the rare moments when he had no alcohol in his system, he became overwhelmed with the feeling of loss. His heart would feel heavy yet empty at the same time, while his mind turned into an echo chamber, the voices of his past taunting him with reminders of his failures.

In short, Tyson was in his own personal hell, with seemingly no way to get out. But, as he would discover later, there actually was.

STUCK IN THE STIGMA

Born to a Filipino mother and Samoan father in Southern California, Tyson had a uniquely blended childhood. Growing up, he would marvel at his father's intricate *Pe'a*, the traditional Samoan tattoo, that spanned from the waist to the knees (Diskin, 2020). He would bake *Fa'apapa* with his grandmother and eat the *adobo* his mother would spend her days off making. Though his parents came from two different cultural backgrounds, they both took the time to try and give Tyson and his three siblings a taste of both heritages. "I loved it," he said to me, tucking his chin-length black hair behind his tan ear. "It opened my eyes to the beauty of different cultures, making me want to read and learn more about other countries and their customs."

One look at Tyson's bedroom would allow anyone to come to that conclusion. Littered around were books on the history of Asia and Europe, CDs of long-ago documentaries on the Egyptians and the Indonesians, and photos of people from around the world. Behind him stood a map of the globe, marked by slanted notes and push pins. I inquired about it.

"Oh," he said, glancing behind him, "those are just the places I want to visit before I die." Suddenly, he hesitated. I arched an eyebrow in question. "But I'm not sure I ever will," Tyson said by way of explanation, shrugging his shoulders, "with my mental illness and everything."

Internally, I grimaced. Why did it have to be like that? There was this misconception that if you had a mental illness, you were *less than*, incapable of doing well for yourself, undeserving of enjoying life's luxuries. Especially with the Asian community's reluctance to seek help and find resources, it becomes hard for those affected by mental illness to think of a reality where they could manage their symptoms and do everything they ever imagined for themselves.

But from the outside, it's always easy to make these remarks. For Tyson, who was still living his mental health journey, it wasn't so straightforward.

"My entire life," he told me, "I've struggled with my mental health. But worse than that, I struggled with a parent who invalidated my mental illness. When you're told that you're just making things up, that you don't need help, *all your life*—it's hard to break away from that mindset [where you believe] that what you have is not real."

Parents, whether they realize it or not, play a large role in whether children seek help and live productive lives with their mental illness. Children often mimic their parents' behaviors, and that includes attitudes toward mental health. If parents are critical and dismissive of their child's mental health symptoms, the child *also* usually becomes dismissive or overly critical of their own struggles. If the parent harbors a strong mental health stigma, in which conversations about mental illness are considered taboo, the child becomes less likely to talk about their mental illness and even less likely to seek help (Rogers Behavioral Health, 2015). In other words, parents can pose a serious barrier to an individual's ability to reach mental wellness.

Regardless, Tyson was now determined to try. To get to this point, however, was nowhere near simple.

DISMISSED AND UNDIAGNOSED: FALLING VICTIM TO THE MODEL MINORITY MYTH

Tyson could never remember a life without mental illness. "It wasn't until college that I was diagnosed with Bipolar II [two] Disorder," he said. "But the symptoms were there since I was young."

Bipolar disorder, according to the Mayo Clinic Staff (2021), is a "mental health condition that causes extreme mood swings that include emotional highs (mania or hypomania) and lows (depression)." There are three main subtypes of bipolar disorder: Bipolar I, Bipolar II, and Cyclothymic disorder. Other variations also exist, such as those that are induced by drugs, alcohol, or medical conditions like Cushing's Syndrome and stroke. A diagnosis of Bipolar I disorder is given when you've experienced "severe mood episodes from mania [a severe form of the emotional high that greatly interferes with daily life, sometimes triggering a break from reality (psychosis)] to depression" (Casarella, 2021; Mayo Clinic Staff, 2021). Bipolar II disorder involves "milder episodes of hypomania [a less extreme form of mania that doesn't usually involve psychosis] that alternate with [sometimes longer] periods of severe depression" (Casarella, 2021; Mayo Clinic Staff, 2021). Cyclothymic disorder is diagnosed when an individual has had "periods of hypomania symptoms and [less severe] depressive symptoms" for at least one (for children and teens) or two (for adults) years (Mayo Clinic Staff, 2021).

Among these three types of bipolar disorder, an individual's diagnosis can further vary based on whether *mixed features* or *rapid cycling* is present. *Mixed features* is a characteristic of bipolar disorder in which the individual experiences depressive *and* manic symptoms at the same time. As in, they'll have high energy and experience sleeplessness, while also feeling hopeless, irritable, and suicidal. *Rapid cycling*, a feature of Tyson's bipolar disorder, refers to an individual who has four or more depressive/manic episodes within a twelve-month period, sometimes even changing between manic to depressive (and vice versa) within a single week or day (Casarella, 2021).

Despite these different types, there are symptoms that are common to all and help guide psychiatrists when giving a diagnosis of bipolar disorder. An individual with bipolar disorder can experience a decreased need for sleep, racing thoughts, increased energy, unusual talkativeness, poor decision-making, abnormally upbeat, jumpy, or wired mood, distractibility, and euphoria (an exaggerated sense of well-being) during their manic periods. During their depressive episodes, feelings of sadness or hopelessness, loss of interest, significant weight loss, decrease or increase in appetite, insomnia or too much sleepiness, restlessness, fatigue, inability to think or concentrate, and suicide contemplation are common symptoms for an individual with bipolar disorder, as well (Mayo Clinic Staff, 2021).

For Tyson, throughout his life, he experienced many of these aforementioned symptoms.

At six years old, rather than mostly playing in a carefree manner with other kids his age, Tyson would hole himself up in his bedroom during his depressive episodes. He would convince himself that everyone hated him, thinking he was unworthy of having any friends. He became snappy, easily irritated by his parents and siblings. Sleep time only brought him nightmares, amplifying the fears and worries that would consume his mind during the day. Then, without any particular rhyme or reason, he would suddenly do a one-eighty, entering into his manic periods. In these weeks, when energy and motivation would strike him, Tyson would almost obsessively be out and about, barely sleeping, always doing something. Whether it was creating piece after piece after piece of artwork or digging for treasure that he just *knew* he was destined to find, Tyson (and his thoughts) would never rest during these high-energy times. After some weeks or months, once again, a switch would flip in his head and he would wake up in the throes of depression once more.

This cyclical behavior continued throughout elementary, middle, and high school. "I would start so many projects during my manic episodes, like writing a novel or starting a new club, only to abandon them when I entered my depressive episodes shortly after," Tyson said. "It was exhausting to experience, and I'd often not perform as well as I wanted to in school, as a result."

Despite the clear signs of struggle, he never received nor sought out help. Even when he was struggling in school, undergoing blatant mood and behavior changes, Tyson's teachers and friends didn't recognize the (relatively obvious) symptoms of his mental illness—nor did he speak out about his struggles. The reason lies in the model minority myth, which paints API folks as individuals with strong familial foundations, strong financial support, parents working in white-collar jobs, and "of sound mind." As we previously discussed in Part 0 of the book, the idea that Asians are a model minority is a myth that ignores the diversity in socioeconomic standing within Asian and Pacific Islander racial groups; the reality is that many API folks experience poverty and instability, which can cause or exacerbate one's mental illness.

This was exactly the case with Tyson. His father worked as a contract construction worker, while his mother worked as a waitress in a restaurant at a neighboring town—both were only making minimum wage, putting him *just* above the poverty line for a family of five. This left Tyson burdened with the extra responsibility of taking care of his younger siblings, a difficult feat considering that he was experiencing symptoms of bipolar disorder (without any tools or treatment) at this time. However, his peers and teachers, the vast majority of whom *weren't* part of the AAPI community, believing in the model minority myth, automatically assumed that Tyson was relatively well-off with a stable home life. "Everyone thought I had nothing worth struggling about," he said, "so they never thought I might have been experiencing a mental illness." (Of course, this is all based on the misconception that an individual cannot experience mental illness if they don't have an overt environmental struggle.) As such, Tyson was never flagged as potentially struggling with his mental health, nor did his friends bother checking in on him.

Not surprisingly, research supports Tyson's experience. According to a study discussed by Dahyeon Kim in her April 2021 article, when "exposed to the model minority stereotype, individuals were less likely to detect clinical symptoms and more likely to perceive better mental health functioning for a member of that group". The stereotypes end up creating a facade that masks the struggles of AAPI folks; it deceives people, leading them to believe Asians and Pacific Islanders do not experience mental illness. As a result, AAPI folks have a high likelihood to be undertreated and underdiagnosed (Kim, 2021).

Unfortunately, even Tyson himself fell victim to the model minority myth, forcing himself to try and uphold an appearance of perfection in *all* aspects, including his mental health. "When you're constantly told that as an individual part of the AAPI community, you have everything in the world," he said to me, "it pressurizes you, almost unknowingly, to adhere to those stereotypes. You don't want to appear as a failure, when the rest of your race seems to meet the expectations. You want to meet those standards, even at the expense of bettering your mental health." This pressure was only compounded by his parents, who, in the rare times they would notice his depressive episodes, would tell him to "get a handle" on himself and to "stop being selfish."

"Because of what they [my parents] would say," Tyson said, "I thought I was being overdramatic, acting up over nothing. I felt like I was already burdening them by not being this perfect, 'mentally stable' son." And so, he remained silent, refusing to acknowledge his struggles or seek help, even though he had an inkling that the feelings and symptoms he was experiencing weren't necessarily healthy. To Tyson, he had a duty to keep up appearances for his family's sake—and there was no one around him telling him otherwise or expressing concern, too caught up in the model minority myth.

It wasn't until Tyson's mental health got much, *much* worse that someone finally spoke up.

REACHING HIS BREAKING POINT

It was like any other day.

The last remnants of winter gave way to the blooming flowers and warm sun of a California spring. A small breeze made its way through the trees, bringing with it a healthy dose of pollen that never failed to make the students of CVHS sneeze. The school bell had rung at noon, dismissing the students early due to their spring break.

Tyson, however, wasn't going home just yet. He still had to go to swim practice, his last one before his team's qualifying match that weekend. Though nearly every fiber of his being wanted to go home and sleep for eternity, he knew he couldn't do such a thing. It was his senior year, and he had just been accepted to quite a prestigious university. If he just let go of swim now, not only would it jeopardize his admission as an athletic recruit (as he believed at the time), but the disappointment his parents would feel would be unimaginable. He refused to ruin the image of perfection he had so carefully curated.

So, with a heavy heart and mind, Tyson dragged himself to practice, expecting his teammates to be in the locker room, dressing into their swimsuits. Instead, what he found were rows of solemn faces, with his coach standing at the front.

"What happened?" Tyson asked, confused at the scene before him.

Tyson's coach looked up at him, teary-eyed. One of his teammates grabbed his arm, as if to steady him for the words about to come out of their coach's mouth.

"Our team member, Darien, passed away early this morning. It was a car accident."

At that moment, life as Tyson knew it shattered. He couldn't breathe. He couldn't think. Tyson stood there, numb, as the voices of his coach and teammates became increasingly distant. His vision tunneled, as he thought about Darien's laugh, Darien's smile. The way Darien would offer him a Snickers bar after practice and make sure to pack extra snacks for Tyson for their games. How Darien would speak of their futures, painting scenes of team reunions and joint family vacations.

The room suddenly became too stuffy for Tyson, the cloyingly sweet smell of Darien's cologne invading his nose. He needed to get out of here.

With shaking legs, Tyson walked out of the locker room, allowing the metal doors to slam behind him. Tears started flowing down his cheeks, starting off as a creek's trickle that quickly turned into a rushing river of snot and saltwater.

It couldn't be real, but it was. Darien, the one who Tyson considered as a brother, as his closest friend and teammate, was gone.

•••

"That's when something in me snapped," Tyson told me, as he thought back to that day.

Up until that point, Tyson had been precariously walking along a razor-thin line, barely maintaining the facade of being unaffected by the cycles of depressive and hypomanic episodes. But now? With the grief of his friend's passing too much to handle, he fell into a deeper depressive state.

"When I learned of my friend's passing," he said, "though I didn't know it at the time, I was already suffering from a depressive episode because of my bipolar disorder. So, when I heard the news about Darien, it just pushed me over the edge."

Tyson became disengaged with the world around him. He intensely isolated himself, not speaking with his family, nor his friends or teammates, about what he was feeling. "I just felt this immense sense of loss," he explained. "I was constantly in pain, emotionally." Feelings of guilt and regret intensified in him, as he simultaneously lost interest in his school and extracurricular work. His mind would echo with memories of Darien, resulting in endless nights without sleep. Within the course of a month, Tyson lost nearly ten pounds— it was difficult for him to find the energy to eat meals, much less wake-up and go to school every day.

In Tyson's case, grief wasn't necessarily a trigger for his depression, but rather something that exacerbated his existing symptoms. For many folks with bipolar disorder, however, grief often can induce a depressive episode, especially for those who experience *rapid cycling*. It can prevent individuals from processing their grief, too caught up in their mood symptoms. Instead of just recovering from just the pain of losing a loved one, they need to also manage their depressive symptoms (Pendulum: Stories and Information, 2020)—a task that can be daunting without support, as Tyson found.

"I didn't know what to do or how to process it all," he told me, "so I started looking for something that would at least dull everything." It didn't take long for him to find the substance that would allow him to do just that; after all, it was the same substance his father used to deal with his own issues: alcohol.

As a depressant (which is something that reduces arousal and stimulation), alcohol can have sedative effects (Alcohol and Drug Foundation, 2021; Hilliard, 2021). It can elicit feelings of calmness, and, when consumed in large amounts, can dull the senses and release feelings of pleasure and reward—an effect that Tyson longed for. However, alcohol as a coping mechanism is dangerous—prolonged and heavy use usually causes memory loss and impaired brain functionality. In more extreme cases, especially when large amounts are consumed in a short amount of time, it can suppress breathing and heart rate, resulting in death (Hilliard, 2021).

"I knew the risks associated with alcohol," Tyson said. "I mean, we went over alcohol and drug abuse in class our freshman year. But when you don't know or have the tools or resources to deal with your mental health symptoms, alcohol—or drugs—becomes this easy solution that can be accessed both quickly and easily. Especially since I saw my father, who, instead of using professional services, would use alcohol to cope with what he was dealing with, I saw it as a ticket out of the mental hell I was experiencing. But as my dependence on it grew, it became hard to fathom another reality."

It would be especially difficult for *anyone*, if they had multiple barriers to seeking help for their grief and mental illness. Thus, considering that the Asian/Pacific Islander populations have quite a few of them (barriers), it comes as no surprise that binge drinking and prescription drug misuse are frequent among AAPI adults with mental illnesses (Mental Health America, 2021)—a sobering reality that is most definitely a cause of concern.

EXPLORING SUBSTANCE ABUSE: AN UNHEALTHY COPING MECHANISM

The relationship between mental health disorders and substance use isn't something new. Studies from the past have found that those with a mental illness are more likely to develop a substance use disorder or use substances. It usually begins in adolescence, which is also when signs of mental illness and a curiosity about illicit substances often appear. Whether due to a lack of understanding about what they're experiencing or a lack of easy access to professional help, many youths turn to drugs and alcohol to cope with their symptoms. Left untreated, it can develop into a substance abuse disorder (National Institute on Drug Abuse, 2021).

However, this understanding of mental illness and substance use often centers around white Americans. For the longest time, substance abuse and dependence within the AAPI community has been ignored. The recent growing number of studies, however, have shown that it is a real issue within the Asian and Pacific Islander populations. According to the United States Department of Health and Human Services (2018), 23.3 percent of Asian/Pacific Islanders suffer from binge drinking *and* a mental illness, 26.7 percent use illicit drugs *and* are diagnosed with a mental illness, and 6.2 percent misused prescription pain relievers *and* had a mental illness. While these rates are still lower than the national averages, we're seeing a general increase in alcohol and drug (mis)use among AAPI folks, especially those aged eighteen to twenty-five (United States Department of Health and Human Services, 2018). This indicates there is a larger problem at play, something that isn't being addressed effectively.

That "something" is the unique cultural stigma around mental health experienced by Asians and Pacific Islanders. Many are reluctant to seek help or to admit they're struggling mentally, in fear of communitywide judgment. Especially for Asian men, for whom emotions and mental struggles are associated with a weak constitution and an even weaker mind, a reality where they use mental health services is incomprehensible. In all of these cases, it leaves people with symptoms that make their day-to-day lives difficult. Thus, with no resources or services to turn to, individuals commonly use substances as a self-medication tool to alleviate such symptoms (Lesser, 2021). Dr. Reddy comments on this. "Unfortunately," Dr. Reddy says, "it is more accepted in many families to use alcohol to silently cope than to openly admit they're struggling and rely on professional services—which ultimately leaves people more susceptible to substance abuse disorders." In essence, the stigma, combined with the rising rates of mental illness, is causing more and more AAPI folks to turn to substances to handle their mental illnesses.

But these substances are nowhere near the best way to deal with one's mental illness, as Tyson can attest to.

A WAKE-UP CALL

"My alcohol use quickly got out of hand," Tyson said.

Sobriety became a faraway dream for him, as a drunken haze became his norm. For nearly four months, he was ensnared by the addictive feeling of numbness alcohol gave him; he was able to go through his day without *feeling* anything too much. It was a temporary fix—one that addressed his symptoms, but not his illness or the source of his grief. "While I felt like I was in bliss at the time," Tyson said, "it wasn't *actually* helping. It was just something that dulled the pain, but it never actually went away."

Though his parents knew of the loss and noticed the rows of empty alcohol bottles in his room, they did little to try to help him. To them, especially his father, there was no real cause for concern; his behavior was just how their family dealt with things. Even his friends and teammates didn't connect him with resources, despite knowing of his constant intoxicated state, each of them still caught in their own grieving process. "That's why I feel so lucky to have had Coach D in my life," said Tyson, the gratitude evident in his eyes. "Without him, I know I wouldn't have recovered."

During this time, Tyson's grades were at an all-time low. During swim practice, his movements would be unsteady; even during their matches, his performance was (as his coach put it) abysmal. Tyson rarely spoke with anyone, only lazily nodding or shaking his head when asked a question. "I think at first," he explained, "Coach D excused it, since we were all still reeling from the loss of Darien." But weeks and weeks went by, with Tyson showing no signs of improving. That's when his coach became concerned.

"It was really random," he remembered. "I was in class, when the intercom went off, telling me to report to Coach D's office." At the time, Tyson was confused, but gathered his stuff and went. "When I arrived, Coach D was just sitting there in his black leather chair, looking at me kindly." What ensued was an hours-long conversation, which ultimately resulted in Tyson confessing about everything that was going on, from his alcohol use to the pain of Darien's death to his cycles of mood-related lows and highs.

"To this day," Tyson said, "I don't know why I decided to confide in him. Maybe it was because he was the first person to reach out to me, to finally show concern." By the end, his coach had one request: Tyson was to speak to his parents about everything he had just told him. His coach believed he needed help, especially for his alcohol use—and the only way to get him to a treatment center, where he could recover under the watchful gaze of trained personnel, work through his grief, and have his mental health evaluated, was through his parents.

But Tyson knew that would pose a large problem, as his previous attempts to broach the subject of his mental health (symptoms) were always met with anger and annoyance. Yet, for his coach, he decided to give it one last shot.

WHY PARENTS AREN'T ALWAYS OUR ALLIES

"It, unfortunately, did not go the way I wanted it to," Tyson said, his mouth thinning into a flat line.

Rather than being open to conversation and hearing his son out, Tyson's father fell into a rage. Substance abuse? Mental health? Those things just didn't exist, as far as his family was concerned.

"He got mad that I would even dare suggest such a thing. He told me there was nothing wrong with me, that I was just making a big deal out of nothing, like usual." At that point, Tyson was used to his father's disparaging remarks. "Neither of my parents ever showed concern about my mental health, so why would they have then?"

But still, it was an upsetting experience for him. "On one hand, there was Coach D, who had reached out to me, listened to me, took me seriously. Then, there were my parents, who ignored me, shut me down, and thought I was overreacting." To Tyson at the time, his parents seemed like the "worst people in the world," especially his father. Though he had one person believe him, not having his parent's support was disheartening. "It made me question, do I *actually* need help, or was I just overreacting?"

Sometimes, parents aren't always someone we can go to for help or support—they can be too caught up in the stigma, too adamant about what they were taught growing up, or too busy dealing with their own issues to be that figure for us. "Sometimes, for some family members, this is their cultural framework," Dr. Lee explains. "It's hard for them to let go of what they've been taught. Other parents have their own issues, their own struggles—so, it's too hard for them to be there for other people, including their kids. We have to accept the reality that your folks may never *ever* get it and support you in the way you need."

If that happens, there is only one thing left to do, Dr. Lee says. You need to ask yourself: *Where else can I look?*

THE PATH TO HEALING BEGINS

That was the same realization that Tyson eventually came to.

"Honestly," he reflected, "I think it was because they themselves hadn't come to terms or dealt with their own mental health struggles. I mean, my father drank, like, [multiple] big bottles a day! That man was clearly going through something, though he would never admit it."

In understanding the root cause of his parents' adverse reactions to his mental health symptoms, substance issues, and attempts at conversation about it all, Tyson was able to begin making peace with the fact that his parents would never be part of his mental health journey. He started to separate his parents' beliefs from his own reality; no longer did he question whether he needed help—he knew he did, and his parents, even though they continued to think otherwise, weren't going to change that. All Tyson needed now was someone else to be that support for him.

"Thankfully, I had Coach D," he said. "And that was enough for me to slowly pull myself out of excessive alcohol use and eventually use mental health services when I got to college that fall."

Over the next few months, while keeping in close contact with his coach, Tyson nursed himself out of his drinking habits. When summer ended and his college career began, the first thing Tyson did was visit his campus's counseling services. The advantage of having access to free mental health services on his campus—a feature that most, if not all, college campuses have—revolutionized his path to mental wellness. "Not only did I get the opportunity to start working through my grief and gain tools to better deal with my depressive cycles, but I also got a referral to see a psychiatrist." Through that psychiatrist, Tyson got his diagnosis of Bipolar II Disorder and started on medication.

"I now had clarity on what I was experiencing and was better prepared to deal with everything as they came," Tyson said, voice animated. "My hypomanic episodes, my depressive episodes—it all became more manageable with my medication, my psychiatrist, and my counselor." After a lifetime of denying his symptoms, then succumbing to substance dependence when faced with loss, it was a scary, foreign process for Tyson to learn to prioritize his mental health and accept professional help. But with Coach D in his corner, it was a process that he didn't have to go through alone.

Today, as a college student in the midst of a global pandemic, Tyson is constantly learning how to take care of his mental health. He still has his "bad" days, in which he sometimes reverts to his old habit of isolating from friends, but his support system (consisting of Coach D and his mental health team) is always there to remind him of the importance of continuing to reach out and using the resources and tools provided to him. Sometimes, Tyson gets caught up in the stigma and stereotypes surrounding mental illness, but he's trying to teach himself to detach the connotations of *mentally weak* and *crazy* from his definition of it—and as allies or individuals struggling with mental health, it's something we need to put effort into doing, too.

We have a responsibility to be more cognizant of the words we use in our day-to-day conversations; ascribing extreme and damaging verbiage when talking about mental health and mental illness contributes to the stigma we see today. When we try to insult someone for changing their mind by calling them "bipolar," or use the word "insane" when describing someone with a mental illness, we're influencing ourselves (and the people around us) into viewing mental health in a negative light. It may not seem like it but changing the way we talk about mental health and illness can make a world of a difference for those struggling; it can help them feel more comfortable in gathering support and more willing to seek help—actions that can ultimately better their lives.

The impact of language is seen in the way Tyson viewed his own mental health struggles for the longest time. Due to the words used by society, his friends, and his parents, Tyson ignored his symptoms and feared seeking professional resources. He even slipped into unhealthy habits, depending on alcohol when his mental health got worse. Luckily for him, a trusted adult stepped in. Now, Tyson is working toward mental wellness, though he is quick to state the hard work isn't over.

"My mental health journey is nowhere near done," he remarked. "I still have so much to learn—and unlearn—in regard to my mental illness and the way I take care of it." Though he still doesn't have the support of his parents, Tyson knows it doesn't mean they love him any less—they are just too caught up in the learned cultural stereotypes and their own untreated issues. What he has decided to focus on, instead, is himself and his recovery.

"I'm thankful that I've started on this journey," Tyson reflected, "and I can't wait to see how much more I progress and grow." The path to getting to this stage has been long and hard, but it is clear there are good things to come for him. It's a future Tyson is looking forward to, as he continues to receive treatment and look after his mental health.

THE BREAKTHROUGH BOX

Sometimes, despite your efforts, your parents may never be your support. However, that does not mean you are undeserving of help. Your symptoms and experiences are valid; you have the right to seek help.

And if you know of someone who doesn't have the support of their parents, step up and be that guiding figure for them. You have the potential to impact their well-being.

PART 4

NORMALIZE THERAPY (AND OTHER MENTAL HEALTH SERVICES)

The mental health journey isn't complete without seeking help.

Admitting that you're struggling, creating your support system, reaching out to your parents—all of these are important steps, but they are ultimately only *part* of the recovery process. Sometimes, true mental wellness cannot be achieved without utilizing professional treatment. Whether that's in the form of therapy, counseling, or medication, it is necessary to be open to and unafraid of seeking professional mental health help.

However, that is always easier said than done. When the world of mental health is stigmatized in many Asian communities, it can feel embarrassing and shameful to use mental health resources or receive treatment. We don't want others to know that we need the help, as we're afraid of being painted as "crazy" or "weak."

However, despite these fears, as Susanna Yee and Caitlin Le show us, it's important to use and speak out about receiving treatment for our mental health. Neither of these individuals was able to achieve mental wellness alone. Both needed professional help to gain the tools, knowledge, and medication necessary—sometimes, more than once. We are *not* weak to need therapy, and we are *not* failures for returning to medication. Rather, it takes true strength to be able to openly admit we need outside help and to *utilize* that help, despite the stigmatization that exists in many AAPI communities.

In other words, Susanna Yee and Caitlin Le are challenging the harmful mental health narrative that has plagued Asian communities for so long—and it's something we can learn to do, too.

If we openly take the plunge into the world of professional mental health services, instead of being reluctant or secretive about using them, we will end up modeling the behaviors that will encourage others to get help, as well. This is how, ultimately, we can create a community more accepting of mental health, mental illness, and seeking treatment.

CHAPTER 9

SUSANNA YEE

——

"I just remember crying in front of her desk, and she's like, 'You might not be able to talk about it just yet.' That sucked to hear because I wanted to process it, but I couldn't do it. I would cry, I would be silent, I would procrastinate on it. I would do a lot of things that normal people don't usually do. But now? I think it's gotten to a point where I can talk about it."

At twenty-eight years old, Susanna Yee first strikes you as an unassuming woman. Her brown, almost black hair falls softly on her shoulders; her cream-colored skin takes on a slightly pink hue from the summer heat that drifts into her bedroom. There is an aura of kindness around Yee, seen in her soft smile and calm demeanor. It's enough to put almost anyone at ease.

But one look into her honey-brown eyes, and you're suddenly pulled down by the heavy sadness that lies within them. Those are the eyes of a woman who's seen too much in her life; those are the eyes of a woman who's lost even more. Deep within the caverns of pain, however, there is a glimmer of possibility...a slight hint of hope and of healing, carefully cultivated from her years-long efforts to better her mental health.

And she's finally ready to reveal how she got to this point.

HAPPY, HUMBLE BEGINNINGS

"In the beginning, it was me, my mom, my dad, my brother, and my grandfather," Yee recounted. "The five of us lived together. It was really nice at first."

Born in Dorchester, Massachusetts, to a Korean father and a Chinese mother, Susanna Yee was the elder of the Yee siblings. Expected to be a responsible role model, she was generally a very obedient child growing up. "Between the two of us, my younger brother was probably the one who misbehaved more," she said. "So, I tried my best to do well in school and help my brother along." Especially seeing her parents work hard to provide for her and her sibling, she wanted to pay them back in some way. And for Yee, that meant succeeding academically.

During the first few years they lived in Dorchester, her father worked for IBM and her mother as a waitress at a local restaurant. "Because of them," Yee said, "we had a nice life." However, that stability didn't last forever.

"My father had a bit of a temper," she said. And that temper was what landed the Yee family in hot water, disrupting life as they knew it. "A fellow employee had called him [my father] racial slurs during work one day." Angered, her father broke that employee's leg. Needless to say, he was subsequently fired. "We ended up having to move out of our house," Yee said. "But we didn't move very far—just to a place across Fields Corner Station. It was quite convenient for high school and college, actually." But it was still a relatively rougher neighborhood to live in. "There was a good amount of violence in the area at the time I was growing up there," she described. If her parents had their way, they wouldn't have been living there; however, it was the only place they could afford in the area.

Unable to find a high-enough paying job following his termination at IBM, her father began to sell cigarettes on the side. Her mother took on extra responsibilities, working extra shifts as a waitress while taking care of the kids and their sickly grandfather. Yee, wherever and whenever she could, would help, watching over her brother or assisting her mother in the kitchen. "It wasn't the best of scenarios, but we made it work. My parents did a lot to keep us afloat."

Despite its difficulties, Yee didn't have any reason to complain. At least she had her parents, her brother, and her grandfather with her—close by and safe.

But that all changed, right when she was on the verge of adulthood.

A SUDDEN LOSS AND THE AFTERMATH

It was a gray, overcast morning. The school bus stood out like a beacon, its yellow color bright against the darkened skies. The lettering on the side of the bus was faded, starting to chip away after years of bringing kids to and from school.

A small mass of students was gathered at the corner of the sidewalk. When the bus opened its doors, the students quickly formed a short line, filing in. Susanna Yee, just shy of eighteen at this time, stepped forward, falling into place with the rest of her classmates. Her black backpack was slung across her back, sagging with the weight of the books and forms she had to turn in. It was the day before her high school graduation and attendance was mandatory. Her teacher's warning rang in her mind like a church bell, loud and incessant: *You won't graduate if you don't come to school the day before graduation.*

When Yee stepped onto the bus, her eyes automatically scanned the rows for an empty seat. Almost zombie-like, she dragged herself to the back of the bus, sliding in. She kept her face forward, letting her brown hair fall forward like a shield. The bus shook with the boisterous movements of her classmates, their excitement for the end of the school year palpable. But Yee couldn't bring herself to share the sentiment. The sadness and grief that had escaped her last night were now crashing down on her in full force. The roads passed by in a blur, as salty tears fell down her cheeks.

Suddenly, the bus came to a halt and opened its doors. They had arrived at school. Yee stepped off, keeping her chin tucked down, the tears still not stopping. She had just entered the library when she felt a hand reach out and grab her—it was her friend, Dominique.

"Hey," Dominique said, concern etched onto her face. "What's wrong? Why are you crying?"

Yee glanced up at her friend. "I think my father is dead," she said, her voice trembling ever so slightly. *Dead.* As in, gone from this world. No longer living. No longer breathing.

"Oh my God," Yee heard her friend vaguely say. Suddenly, she was being pulled through the crowd of students, into the office. "You need to go home."

•••

"That day, they sent me home," Yee told me. "I remember the only thing I kept asking was whether I would be able to graduate."

The night before, as she was returning from her friend's house, Yee received a phone call from her brother. What he told her left her frozen and shocked. "He told me our father had been stabbed," she recalled. "I didn't understand how that could've happened." It turned out her father had been having an affair with another woman outside of her mom. The woman her father was seeing was in an abusive relationship; because of that, her father ended up going to the estranged boyfriend's house, causing an altercation. "They got into a fight, which ended up with my dad getting stabbed," Yee explained. He was almost immediately rushed into the ER, but, sadly, passed away later that night. Her mother, grandfather, and brother were immediately distraught, but Yee couldn't bring herself to cry that entire night.

It wasn't until the next morning, on her way to school, that she really began to understand and process what had transpired the night before. That's when all her emotions came rolling through, leaving her feeling exhausted and confused about her future. "I even started questioning if I should go to college," said Yee. "But I had wonderful, supportive friends that reminded me that I had always wanted to go to college, that I *should* go to college." So, that's exactly what she decided to do.

After her father's passing, Yee graduated from high school and started preparing for her college career at the Massachusetts School of Art and Design. "I studied graphic design," she said, a smile forming on her lips, as she remembered her days on campus. "It was really good. I had a really good experience there."

While she stayed in a college dorm for her freshman year, the rest of Yee's family continued to stay in their little house by Fields Corner Station. In an effort to make rent and pay the bills, her mother rented out some of their house's rooms. "We would sometimes get into arguments with those people renting inside the house," she said, "but it was still generally a peaceful life." Yee was going to class, learning new skills, making new friends—it should have all been wonderful, a fresh start after the tragedy of her father's death. *But it wasn't.* There was still one thing that gnawed at the edges of her mind, one thing that left her emotionally drained most days, one thing that just wouldn't let her move forward: her father's court case.

Over the duration of her freshman fall semester of college, Yee and her mother had to attend court. "It was because my dad was involved in what was essentially a homicide case," she said, by way of explanation. What ensued were days of hearings, testimonies, and presentations of evidence. It was a tiring process to relive the trauma and grief of her father's death over and over and over again. And ultimately? It was a process that felt like it only ended in vain when the verdict was delivered. "He [the man who had stabbed my father] ended with a verdict of *not guilty*," Yee said with a slight frown, "so he didn't do any time. Of course, my father was the one who came to his house, but it was still rough seeing him not be held accountable at all."

Through all of this, she found her mental health becoming worse and worse.

TESTING THE WATERS OF THERAPY
"I felt suffocated."

From her father's death to the start of college to the criminal case trial, it was as if life was throwing one hardship after another at Yee. As she became overwhelmed by these events, she increasingly isolated herself, unable to express what she was going through. Her days were accompanied by constant numbness and immense loneliness. "I was just in a bad place."

At first, she didn't know what to do. Her family had never spoken about mental health, and it didn't seem like they would be open to the conversation either; after all, the adults in her life never had *time* to worry about it. "My mom was always working," Yee said. "She was a waitress, she had to take care of my grandfather, she had to provide for my brother and I—she didn't have the luxury to sit down and take care of her mental health." On the other hand, her grandfather, a World War II veteran, would use alcohol as a coping mechanism; it was the only way that he knew how to handle his issues. "He couldn't go anywhere without it. I realized that's not what people usually do—it was alcoholism." Similarly, her brother turned to drugs. No matter where she looked, she wasn't able to see a viable, healthy outlet to process what she was feeling.

This ultimately posed a barrier for Yee. As Mental Health America (2021) states, a "lack of awareness of the resources and services that are available, as well as the stigma surrounding mental health issues, are the biggest deterrents in seeking professional help." That's why most young AAPI folks tend to seek support from "close friends, family members, and religious community members" rather than professional services (Mental Health America, 2021). While your personal network, consisting of friends and family, is most definitely the first line of defense, it is sometimes necessary to expand your support ring. We shouldn't be afraid to use professional services. These services, like therapy and counseling, exist to help us; they can equip us with tools and provide us with a truly safe space that we might be missing.

Though Yee had supportive friends, she didn't feel like she could talk to them about something like mental health. Feelings and emotions were kept private, not shared. But for

Yee, she could no longer do so alone. She *needed* something or someone that would listen to her, while helping her deal with what she was experiencing emotionally.

"That's when," she said, "I remembered seeing people talking about resources on campus, which included a counseling and mental health center. So, I thought to myself, 'You know what? I should probably go talk to somebody about this.'" This was about to be a new experience for her, but it was one she was willing to try. Of course, it helped that her peers would openly speak about their visits to the university's counseling center; having the knowledge that her classmates and friends utilized this resource, and also benefitted from it, helped her feel more at ease in using the service.

From the very first visit, Yee was hooked. "I remember her [my counselor] just, like, being able to talk and sit down with me," she said. "It was weird because I don't think I had ever talked to anyone about these issues before." Everybody at the counseling center was kind and understanding; Yee never felt like she was being judged. With the assistance of her counselor, she slowly improved her mental health. "I would see my counselor once every two or three weeks, and then I would drop in whenever I needed it."

For Yee, counseling (which is a term often interchangeable with therapy) helped her process the events and handle the obstacles life threw at her. It was a space she could regularly visit to voice her feelings and learn how to manage them. Even though she wasn't experiencing a mental *illness*, per se, it was still a useful tool for her to ultimately better her mental health and to deal with her grief. "Everyone, at least at some point of their lives, (...) needs counseling," Nadia Persun writes in a May 2016 article on *PsychCentral*. As we've discussed before, mental health impacts everyone;

we experience a whole range of emotions, including sadness, anxiousness, and fear. These emotions, if not dealt with, can affect our day-to-day lives. That's where therapy and counseling can come in. These two services give people access to "trained mental health professionals who can estimate accurately the scale of [one's] problems, identify their roots and their negative impact, and help [one] map and follow (...) the effective pathway to growth and healing" (Persun, 2016). In essence, when our mental health becomes poor, when we don't know what to do to improve it, professional services can help us do just that.

Therapy, or counseling, comes in all forms—individual, group, family. You can use the sessions to just vent, to reflect, or to learn the tools and practices that can help you manage your emotions as they come (Good Therapy, 2015). In Yee's experience, counseling consisted of all three. "I just remember that time being really valuable to me," she said. "It was a relief to have that resource available to me."

Before she knew it, Yee graduated from college, successfully sticking with one of the hardest programs at her university. "One hundred students would enter my program, but only about fifty graduated," she said. She attributes her success to her counselor and counseling services. "If I didn't have that, I don't know how I would have fared against my classes, to be quite honest." Shortly after, Yee started working with a design team at a fitness start-up. "So, I stopped seeing the counselor at my college because it [the counseling service] was mostly for [current] students."

And, at first, that was okay for Yee. She was flourishing at her job, working on exciting projects, and able to help provide for her family. She also had the tools to handle daily challenges, along with friends that would check in on her and each other. She had support, and her life had become relatively stable, so there seemed to be no need for her to utilize a mental health service. After all her hardships, it was a nice state to be in.

Then, tragedy struck. Twice.

SINKING IN SORROW

First, it was her grandfather.

It happened suddenly, but not unexpectedly. For the past almost five years, Yee's grandfather had been at a nursing home due to his declining health. So, when she received the news that her grandfather had passed, it did not necessarily come as a great surprise. After years of battling alcoholism and associated health issues, it was amazing he had managed to hold on for this long; though she was saddened by his death, she was thankful for all the time she had with him.

Now, with just her, her mom, and her brother left, the three decided to move to Malden, Massachusetts. "It was a nice change of pace," she said. "It was quieter there." Their new home held a calm that helped to put her mind at ease—a welcome effect, especially after the past few tumultuous weeks. Slowly, life started to settle into a stable routine again, the pain of loss finally beginning to dull. Yee felt like she could breathe again, her heart no longer as heavy. But just as quickly that reprieve came, another harrowing life event came hurtling at her.

Then, it was her mom.

It started with an inability to remember things. As a young woman in her late thirties, who worked as a waitress, her mom's forgetfulness struck her as unusual. However, she didn't think too much about it, initially. "But then, one day, she was just sitting on the kitchen floor, not saying anything."

Concerned, Yee asked if everything was okay, but her mother wouldn't respond. "We had to go to the hospital that day," she said. "She wasn't talking and seemed to be unable to walk also. To see someone so able-bodied suddenly *not* be... it was scary."

Her mom was immediately wheeled off to various diagnostic rooms. When the doctors came back from running some tests, their faces were grim. Unbeknownst to Yee until that moment, her mom had preexisting breast cancer, which had spread to her liver and her brain. She had chosen not to tell Yee and her brother about her breast cancer diagnosis nor her treatment from nearly a decade ago. "It wasn't until I learned about this that I realized that the short, cropped hair my mom had in some of our photos was because she was going through radiation at the time." With all the hardships their family had faced, Yee's mother didn't want to burden her children with her illness; at the same time, being the main breadwinner of their family after her husband's passing, she didn't bother herself with her health.

But that couldn't continue.

"We immediately started her on radiation," Yee informed me. After about two weeks, her mother was no longer in that nearly comatose state; the radiation had helped to shrink the brain tumor's swelling drastically. "She became more like herself," Yee remembered. "She was smiling, laughing. She was like my regular mom again." That rosy imagery didn't last too long, unfortunately. Shortly after beginning radiation, the side effects began manifesting in her mother, and, suddenly, Yee was thrust into the caretaker role.

While balancing work and ensuring that the rent and bills were paid, Yee tended to her mom's needs. She'd help feed and dress her mother, clean up the vomit, and accompany her to all doctor's visits. Just like how her mother had supported their family, she was now doing the same.

Eventually, however, Yee realized she couldn't keep her mother at the house any longer. Her mother's condition was only getting worse, and her house didn't have the accessibility and constant supervision her mom needed. They would've needed to have her bed refitted into a medical structure—something they didn't have the means to do; her mother needed to have her medication administered every couple of hours, which was hard with Yee's work schedule.

"I had to make the difficult decision to keep her at a nursing home," Yee said, "since I knew our health insurance would cover that." Along with her friend, Yee visited multiple nursing homes until she found one that was convenient to drive to and affordable. She ultimately found one in West Roxbury, about forty-five minutes from their home. "Every morning before work, I would drive there and spend about an hour with her. I would make sure she had everything she needed, bring fresh laundry and stuff from the house." But her mother never enjoyed her time at the nursing home, especially as one of the youngest patients there. "She was pissed!" Yee exclaimed. "She hated the bed, she hated everything." But she had no other choice, no other way to ensure her mother was properly taken care of. And so, her mother continued to stay at the nursing home and Yee continued to visit her mother every morning.

It had become part of their daily routine—until it no longer was.

"I'm just glad, until the very end, she had such caring staff around her at that place. I hope that we were able to extend her comfort." Early one morning, Yee received a phone call. It was the nursing home, informing her that her mother had passed away during the night. In that moment, Yee's world shattered. "Her death was especially difficult because my mom was like our rock," she said, her voice trembling. "I didn't realize it at first—I thought it was my grandfather, but no. It was my mom. She held our family together, she helped keep us going." In between planning her mother's funeral, Yee was spiraling in a sea of sadness and hopelessness. These feelings were only compounded by her company, which decided to let go of her just two weeks after her mother's funeral. "[My] company had been going through a transition, so they shuffled around a lot of employees," she explained.

At around twenty-two years old, Yee had no more living parents and no job. She had officially reached her breaking point. "I *literally* had to talk to somebody," she related, "or I was going to lose my mind." Her friends and ex-coworkers would check up on her occasionally, but that wasn't enough for her to pull herself out of those feelings of numbness, sadness, and grief. "I didn't know how to figure this all out," Yee said.

So, she turned to the one place that had helped her, back in college.

REVISITING THE PAST TO SECURE A BETTER FUTURE

"I actually emailed the head of counseling at MassArt [my university]," Yee recounted.

Though she was an alumnus and no longer a current student, Yee knew that the counseling center would be able to help her. "I asked if I could call and talk to [her]," she said. The counselor responded within just a couple of days, saying yes. They then hopped on a phone call, where she explained how her mom had recently passed away, not too long after her father and grandfather. She mentioned that she felt like she needed counseling or therapy, to talk it all out. "I couldn't continue living like this."

In being vulnerable and candid about where she was at, and relating that with a trusted individual, Yee unlocked help that transformed her life. "She [my counselor] actually went up and out of her way to find a therapist for me," she said, the gratitude evident in her voice. Her counselor even took the extra step to connect her with an Asian American woman as her therapist, in an effort to ensure that Yee would feel comfortable and relate better. Thankful and eager, she reached out to the therapist immediately. "I started seeing her every week."

Even though she had been through counseling at her university, it was still a challenging process getting to a state of relative mental wellness. "At first," Yee said, "I wanted to process it quickly. I wanted to eat up these feelings, then ship them out, and have that be done with. But it doesn't really work out like that."

As Yee learned through therapy, mental wellness is a continuous process; it requires you to take the time and make the space to talk about and work through what is affecting you. It necessitates being cognizant of your mental state and willing to reach out for help when needed. "There were a number of things that I don't think I had been addressing," said Yee. But with her therapist, she finally could. "I was able to talk through my feelings and figure out where I wanted to be. I learned how I was processing things and became aware of how it was going for me."

But the benefits didn't stop there for her. Not only did her therapist help her learn how to get through her bad days, but she also helped Yee become more confident in telling her mental health story. "We worked through it until I was ready to tell my friends, then a reporter, and now you."

HER FINAL MESSAGE

"Currently, I don't see a therapist," Yee said.

After years of being with the same one, Yee had to, unfortunately, cease visiting her therapist, when she lost her job (and her health insurance). "But what's nice about the number of years I had been seeing my therapist," she revealed, "is that it's given me a lot of strategies on how to work through everything without degrading my well-being. I am really grateful that I had my therapist and my counselor." Without therapy, without being willing to use mental health services, Yee wouldn't have reached this state of well-being and preparedness. She now is able to tackle her bad days while enjoying the good ones.

"A lot of our [AAPI folks'] shared experiences surround the idea where if you do well, get a good job, and brute force it through, you'll be fine. But nobody tells you that you have to deal with all of that while fighting this inner demon that will just inconveniently come out of nowhere, at the worst times." For Yee, that demon came out quite a bit over the past decade. Without those services and the support of her friends, Yee is sure she wouldn't have been able to get through everything that had happened in her life. That's why she takes every opportunity today to emphasize the importance of using mental health services, whether or not one is diagnosed with a mental illness.

"You need to know," Yee advised, "that you need to give yourself the care you so willingly give to your dear friends." Seek that therapist, go to the counselor, talk to others about how you're feeling, check in with your friends about their mental health, recommend people to use professional resources. That's how we can slowly normalize the use of mental health services—the same services that helped Susanna Yee, the young woman from Dorchester, Massachusetts, who loved to draw and design and who had lost so much.

THE BREAKTHROUGH BOX

Professional help and mental health are relevant to everyone. You don't need to have a mental illness to use mental health services. Whether for a lifetime or for just a moment, sometimes you will need that extra help, those professional resources. So, use them. They can help make those difficult times—those periods of poor mental health—more manageable.

CHAPTER 10

CAITLIN LE

———

She stared at the clock. *Tick, tock. Tick, tock.* The bottle of pills she had brought back from her psychiatrist appointment earlier that day stood silent on her dresser, its white plastic sheen dulled by the darkness of her room. Her floor was littered with piles of books, papers, and clothes—she hadn't had the motivation to clean it for days. Even now, her body ached with fatigue, unwilling to come out of bed, despite doing almost nothing. Dried tears stained her golden cheeks, as heavy emotions continued to swirl in her gut.

Despite her best efforts, twenty-three-year-old Caitlin Le had hit a depressive low, again. The COVID-19 restrictions had taken a toll on her mental health, making her feel isolated, alone, and caught in a deep sense of sadness. To add to that, her anxiety was making even the smallest of tasks difficult to complete. She knew she couldn't deal with her mental health through sheer will anymore; she needed help. Yet, Le found herself hesitating.

She had been doing so well without the assistance of her antidepressants. She was a full-time graduate student, studying to become an audiologist. She had removed a toxic individual from her life and surrounded herself with supportive friends and family. She had even begun openly speaking about her hearing disability on a public platform, inadvertently becoming an advocate.

But now, after a mere two-month quarantine period, Le's depression was rearing its ugly head. Part of her felt ashamed by her inability to power through and maintain the mental wellness she had achieved since the year prior; the other part acknowledged that she couldn't endure this any longer. Ultimately, the entirety of Le was caught in a dilemma of how to move forward.

Le eyed the bottle of pills, as one thought echoed in her mind: *Should I take the medication?*

EARLY SIGNS OF MENTAL ILLNESS

Caitlin Le's first brush with mental illness started in late high school. Senior year, to be exact.

"It started with a panic attack," she said.

One day, during the fall of her senior year, Le was spending time with friends in the backyard. Someone had brought BB guns—air guns that shot plastic pellets—and jokingly aimed one in her general direction. "Suddenly, I couldn't breathe," Le recounted. "I was crying, shaking, the whole nine yards. But I had no idea what was going on."

With the assistance of her friends, she was ultimately able to calm down. However, she didn't delve much into why or what had triggered the panic attack, nor did she explore how it could be related to any underlying mental health conditions. She had already been the target of bullying in the past due to her hearing loss; the last thing she wanted to do was call attention to another "abnormal" thing about her. "When you have a hidden disability, you're already like 'I have to be normal.' So, you feel like you can't talk about it [your mental health]," Le explained.

It also didn't help that Le at the time didn't have a clear idea about what even *constituted* as mental health. Both in her community and at her school, there was virtually no conversation about what mental health and mental illness was. The Vietnamese Catholic community her family belonged to didn't believe in the concept of mental health, so it was never spoken about in that space. At school, it was mentioned briefly in their freshman year health class, but nothing more. The little awareness she had come from her friends. "Somehow, I always drew in people who had mental health [struggles] going on, since middle school. Like my best friend would self-harm," Le mentioned. However, they never knew what to do or who to turn to about it, even as they went through high school; it was just something they endured.

It wasn't until her undergraduate career that she learned of the resources and services available—but that only happened after her mental health had gotten worse.

TRIGGERS, GUILT, AND HIGH-FUNCTIONING MENTAL ILLNESS

When Le entered her sophomore year of college, she became trapped in a toxic relationship. Her boyfriend at the time would continually gaslight her, making her doubt her own sanity. "It was really my toxic relationship that brought my [mental illness symptoms] out."

What used to be the occasional bout of anxiousness turned into an incessant gnawing feeling at the pit of her stomach. Her periodic moments of self-doubt transformed into a persistent nagging voice that whispered messages of hopelessness and futility. Every time her boyfriend would plant a seed of doubt in her, she'd spend that night feeling even lower than before. These emotions were similar to what she experienced in high school—but more intense and a lot more constant. "That's when I started thinking maybe there was something deeper affecting my day-to-day thinking," said Le—perhaps depression or anxiety.

Despite recognizing there was likely something wrong, Le didn't seek out help at first. "I felt guilty considering that I might be depressed or struggling with my mental health," she said. She didn't believe what she was experiencing warranted a visit to a professional. Her own understanding of mental illnesses was of ones that visibly affected daily function—depression that led to failing grades, anxiety that prevented one from socializing with friends, schizophrenia that resulted in auditory and visual hallucinations. In Le's case, however, she was still able to maintain her friendships, perform well in school, work part-time, and get through her day; they were just accompanied by an unending stream of negative, depressing thoughts and never-ending feelings of anxiousness.

As Le would later learn, what she was experiencing was typical of high-functioning anxiety and high-functioning depression. The term *high-functioning* refers to the ability to go about most of your daily activities (like work, getting dressed, attending school, managing finances, etc.), without being hindered (YoungMinds' Blog, 2019). With a *high-functioning* mental illness, the individual experiences many of the symptoms associated with the mental health disorder, but it doesn't cause *obvious, observable* disruptions in their lives. Instead, the symptoms are often hidden, experienced almost entirely internally (Bridges to Recovery, n.d.).

Now, the idea of a high-functioning mental illness is something relatively new and still being explored. As we may recall from Chapter 1 and Chapter 3, by current definition, a mental health disorder is diagnosed when the individual's symptoms are interfering with their ability to function (Mayo Clinic Staff, 2019); that *inability to function* is the defining characteristic. However, more and more mental health professionals are starting to recognize the existence of high-functioning mental illness. After all, mental illness is ultimately a spectrum—the way it impacts individuals will vary. Simply because a person can hold a job or manage tasks *doesn't* mean they aren't experiencing difficulty in doing so. Oftentimes, with high-functioning mental illnesses, the individual doesn't perform at their full potential; they experience a reduced ability to live in a "productive, healthy, and satisfying way" (Mental Health Center @ DH, 2017; Bridges to Recovery, n.d.)—which is exactly what was happening with Le.

Left untreated, Le's symptoms persisted, making each day increasingly difficult to complete. It got to a point where she was having silent panic attacks at night, in her then-partner's arms. Intrusive thoughts that imagined worst-case scenarios and incited feelings of paranoia kept her awake at night. "It was very, very hard," she said. "And my ex-boyfriend wasn't very encouraging of my mental health, either. He'd weaponize it."

Despite this, Le found herself unable to take the next step to reach out for professional help. She continued to suffer in silence—that is, until she was in graduate school.

FINDING HOPE IN HER DIAGNOSIS

January 2019 was the start of Le's spring semester in graduate school.

Still in her first year, she was looking forward to continuing to work with patients, similar to last fall. Though her mental health wasn't the best, she was able to manage it. "Then," Le said, her voice taking on a serious tone, "something big happened in my relationship, causing me to have a full-blown depressive episode."

Tears, soul-crushing feelings of empty loneliness and heavy sadness, loss of appetite—Le was suffering from the depths of depression, her anxious thoughts only adding fuel to the flame. The pressures of graduate school, unnecessary comparisons to peers, and a struggling relationship all contributed to Le feeling lower than ever before. "I remember crying before bed or in the car on the way to school," she recounted, "almost every day during that time."

Le didn't recognize herself anymore. "So," she said, "I decided I would go to the psychiatrist."

After five years of denying her symptoms and struggles, Le was ready to embrace professional help. After taking a couple of surveys and answering some questions, she received her diagnosis: generalized anxiety disorder and depression.

Known as the most common mental illness in the United States (Anxiety & Depression Association of America, 2021), anxiety disorders are an entire class of disorders in the DCM, ranging from agoraphobia (a fear and avoidance of places and situations that might cause you to panic and feel trapped or embarrassed) to panic disorder (episodes of sudden intense feelings of anxiety, fear, or terror). *Generalized* anxiety disorder (or GAD, for short) includes "persistent and excessive anxiety and worry about activities or events—even ordinary, routine issues" (Mayo Clinic, 2018). It often manifests with depression, as was the case with Le (Mayo Clinic, 2018).

GAD often develops very slowly, starting during adolescence or young adulthood. Women are twice as likely to be affected by GAD compared to men (Anxiety & Depression Association of America, 2021). Common symptoms include: worrying about everyday things, feeling restless and having trouble relaxing, having trouble falling or staying asleep, feeling tired all the time, feeling "on edge," sweating a lot or being out of breath all the time, and having trouble controlling worries and feelings of nervousness. Often, those with GAD experience physical symptoms, which have the potential to impede one's ability to complete daily activities (National Institute of Mental Health, 2016). It is ultimately a treatable disorder that is experienced by over 6.8 million adults (Anxiety & Depression Association of America, 2021).

When asked about how she felt receiving the diagnosis, Le answered, "I felt validated. I could start attacking it [my anxiety and depression], start working on it." After growing up thinking there was something wrong with her, feeling like her mind wasn't a safe place, it was a relief to know what was affecting her—as it meant that there was a path to feeling *good* again.

Armed with her diagnosis, Le and her psychiatrist decided to treat her depression first. "I started on Lexapro [an antidepressant medication]," she said. "Luckily, I adjusted to it pretty quickly. It took me only two or three days to get over the side effects." Within a week, she was already starting to see the effects of the medication take hold. "Normally, it took a lot out of me to get out of bed in the morning, motivation-wise," she explained. "When I took my antidepressant, it just gave me a jumpstart. I was able to wake up." Along with that, Le experienced elevated mood and felt less fatigued. The anxious thoughts dulled into weak whispers at the back of her mind, while those feelings of hopelessness dwindled into a snuffed flame. She felt more like herself again.

She was also supposed to try therapy, but she hadn't been able to successfully implement it into her life. Regardless, with the help of the medication, after nearly a lifetime of symptoms, Le was feeling much better.

But six months after she started on her medication, she stopped.

FINDING MENTAL WELLNESS—THIS TIME, WITHOUT MEDICATION

In July of 2019, Le found out her boyfriend was cheating on her. It was an unimaginable betrayal, only made more painful after months of being told her suspicions were false and unwarranted. Finally deciding enough was enough, she broke up with him.

"I immediately scheduled a psychiatrist appointment," Le said, as she remembered that day. "I knew that this [the breakup] was going to wreck me. I mean, I was with him for five and a half years!" Her psychiatrist recommended she increase her medication dosage.

At first, she complied. "But by that third day," Le said, "my discernment kicked in. I realized I was sad because I was tied to this guy that continued to hurt me, who I was constantly paranoid about." With that realization, she began forgetting to take her medication. Soon, weeks were going by without Le taking her pills—or experiencing her mental health symptoms. "I realized [even without the medication], I felt good. I was happy. The human that was the direct cause of my depression was no longer in my life. So, I decided not to take them anymore."

While it is wonderful that Le saw improvements in her mental health even without her medication, it is not recommended to stop medication without first consulting your psychiatrist. It might have worked for Le because her depression seemed to be triggered by certain environments (specifically, in this case, her boyfriend), but there's no guarantee the same would happen for everyone else, even if in a similar situation. It's important to have a comprehensive assessment before discontinuing medication, along with conversations on *how* the medication will be stopped; doing so independently and suddenly, or "cold turkey," can lead to many adverse (even life-threatening) reactions. Remember, coming off of medication is usually a long process that is best done gradually and under the supervision of a medical professional (Tartakovsky, 2016).

Even so, for Le, after nearly a year since stopping her medication, she continued to experience mental well-being. Her life was moving forward in a positive direction, and she had created an environment for herself that supported her mental health.

But then, the coronavirus hit.

A RAPID DECLINE

Two weeks after the official shutdown on March 11, 2020, Le found herself dipping into the pools of depression once again. "I missed being in the clinic, I missed school, I missed my friends and my patients. I hit a funk." She was feeling lonely, feeling exhausted...all the symptoms that Le had prior to seeing her psychiatrist and taking her medication were coming back.

At first, she tried to fight the feeling, determined to prove that she didn't need treatment anymore. She attempted to push herself into being productive and energetic, to redirect her thoughts into a less negative direction—but it was all to no avail. As the statewide shutdown stretched from weeks into months, with no clear end in sight, her mental health only got worse. "I'm tired, I'm sad, I'm not doing anything," Le described. It was clear—her lone efforts weren't working. Her determination to feel better wasn't going to be enough this time.

"I got tired of feeling tired," she said. Medication had helped her once, providing her with the mental reprieve she needed. It was a professional treatment and service that existed to benefit her.

She knew what she had to do.

MAKING THE RIGHT DECISION

Le reached out to the bottle, popping open the white top. She shook two oval orange pills into her palm, then grabbed a glass of water.

Le now realized it wasn't weak of her to need her medication again. Mental health and mental illness don't follow a linear path; there will be times when her symptoms will worsen, when she will need to seek out treatment once more. What's important is that she *recognizes* when she can no longer do it on her own, so that she can utilize the services available to her. In doing so, she will be able to better her mental health and manage her symptoms, time and time again.

Le tilted her head back, allowing the pills to fall into her mouth, immediately chasing them with water. Now, she would let this medication do its thing.

THE BREAKTHROUGH BOX

While non-medicative treatments (like therapy and counseling) are important, you should not be afraid of using (or returning to) medication to manage your symptoms and better your mental health. Staying consistent with your treatment can lead to better outcomes in the long run.

CONCLUSION:
LET'S TALK

———

Contending with reality, creating your support system and finding your resources, looking to your parents as allies, normalizing therapy and other professional mental health services—while I acknowledge that help and recovery look different for everyone, these are the steps I've realized that make up the core of most people's mental health journeys. These are the steps the individuals of this book experienced as they worked (and continue to work) to improve their own mental health.

Sara Ahmed and James showed us the journey to mental wellness only begins after we've realized we need help. Although the stigmas that exist in Asian American communities can make us reluctant to admit it, we will not be able to manage our illness or alleviate our symptoms without coming to terms with the fact we're struggling. Only once we move past the denial can the journey begin.

Halima Khan and Sonya exemplified what it means to rely on others. It's important to have a support system, whether made of friends or family, for help to manage our mental health disorders/struggles in times when we're unable to do so ourselves. We must personally search for our resources when we do not have access to professional help—whether that's online or through other spaces (like school or work).

Mirabelle Lei and Tyson walked us through how we may be able to transform our parents into allies—all while showing us why sometimes, they're not. Our parents can be too swept up in their own traumas and mental health struggles, bound by the ideals passed on to them from their parents. In these cases, sometimes it is up to us to begin the conversation, so that the whole family can experience better mental health. But we need to understand that these efforts may not always be successful, and that is okay.

Susanna Yee and Caitlin Le took the brave step in modeling how we too should be unafraid to access resources like therapy, counseling, and medication. Support and self-awareness can only get us so far. Sometimes, we need to utilize professional help, as those resources can equip us with tools to better manage our mental health. Even if we may not necessarily be struggling with our mental health, it isn't wrong to utilize these resources; after all, much like how we exercise and take our vitamins to protect our physical health, services like therapy and counseling can help us protect our mental health, too.

Ultimately, these eight stories, consisting of the experiences and truths of more than twenty people, impart important lessons and showcase that mental health and illness aren't something we should be afraid of. This brings me to the final step of any mental health journey: speaking out.

Much like the people featured in this book, we must share our stories and experiences to help eradicate the stigma that persists in our communities. This is how we inform, in order to transform; we have to be willing to talk. By speaking with each other, with our families, and with our larger communities, we'll start to create an environment that helps others feel more comfortable in seeking out resources. We'll be better prepared to support and know what to do as we encounter friends, family, and peers struggling with their mental health. And most importantly, it will allow us to normalize mental illness and mental health—something the Asian American community sorely needs.

Already, we're seeing incredible people from the API community do just that. Meet Zilin, a current medical student at the University of Massachusetts. She's the founder of Project Harmonious, a program that strives to bridge the cultural and language gaps that often prevent the Chinese community from understanding mental health and illness. More specifically, along with sharing important resources and creating awareness around the importance of mental health, the team collects and shares the stories of Asian Americans, translating their words into Chinese. It's in this way that Zilin and her team ensure that *all* individuals from the Chinese community are able to access the stories that will help them understand each other and develop empathy.

Unsurprisingly, because of the conversations the team has started through Project Harmonious, they've already seen some change. "I'll be on WeChat [a Chinese messaging and social media platform used by many Chinese Americans] and see some of our posts and translated stories shared," Zilin told me. "We're seeing there is a greater conversation around mental health because now these stories and information are accessible, without a language barrier in the way."

Rather than being a hidden topic, mental health is slowly transforming into a public conversation because of projects like Harmonious. Instead of surrounding themselves in a shroud of silence, folks from the Chinese community are taking the brave step to talk about their mental illness. By simply sharing stories, Zilin and her team have shown how community members can work together to raise awareness about and normalize mental health.

But the positive impacts of speaking about our experiences don't end there. In sharing our mental health journeys, it can also encourage others from the AAPI community to seek help. Riya is just one of many examples of this.

Born in Texas, Riya has always had a passion for tennis. While her peers spent their weekends out shopping with friends, she would be on the court with her coach, practicing her forehand swings and serves. But as a woman, the world of sports wasn't necessarily a friendly place. Her coach would nitpick on her body and weight, commenting how "fat" Riya was and how she would be able to run faster if she "just lost weight." Her parents would even sometimes criticize her eating habits, making mindless remarks on when she would help herself to a second serving or desert. Combined with the pressure to be "perfect," as her family and society demanded of her as an Asian American student-athlete, Riya quickly fell into an eating disorder and depression. However, at the time, she didn't realize that was what she was experiencing.

"No one talked about mental health or mental illness in my community," Riya said. "Not my school, not my peers, not my family. No one." The little knowledge she *did* have came from the media, which grossly overdramatized it into something that Riya didn't recognize in herself. So, for years, she simply endured her mental health struggles, never seeking help.

But that all changed when she entered college. "I met people who were suddenly super open about mental health and their experiences with it." Her friends would confide in her about their eating disorders or mental illnesses, talking to her about the resources they used. "My eyes became open to the reality of mental health—and that's how I understood that what *I* had experienced nearly all my teenage life was a mental illness." For Riya, without the people around her being open and talking about their experiences, she would have never realized that she too needed help. It opened up the possibility of a new reality for her—one where she experienced mental wellness. "Thanks to my friends, I was able to take the next step of reaching out for help through my college's counseling department."

This is the importance of storytelling, the importance of speaking our mental health truths.

With the rate of suicide rising among Asian youth and an increasing number of Asian Americans falling victim to substance abuse, it is clear that if we allow the mental health stigma to continue to exist, we'll only jeopardize the health and safety of future generations. We shouldn't be seeking mental health help as a last resort, after it's become extremely severe; it should be the first thing we do when we realize we're struggling.

As we've learned through the course of this book, mental illness *isn't* scary and mental health *is* something that should be prioritized. You're not "weak" or a "failure" just because you struggle with your mental health; it's not "shameful" to have a mental illness. Mental illness is just *one* part of a person—it doesn't change the fact that they have hopes, passions, and dreams. It doesn't make them subhuman or take away from their kindness, compassion, and strength.

It is possible to lead healthy, productive lives when diagnosed with a mental health disorder—it's just up to us to seek help to ensure that we learn to manage our symptoms and better our mental health. By doing this for ourselves, we can inspire others around us to do the same. By encouraging our families and our peers to seek help, we can contribute to a community environment that normalizes mental health, rather than stigmatizing it. By learning of the barriers AAPI folks face, we can be better allies and a more culturally sensitive support system for Asian Americans and Pacific Islanders across the nation.

This book is my attempt at creating such a reality. What will you do?

RESOURCES FOR FURTHER EXPLORATION

For more information on mental health, mental illness, and resources, please visit:

- *www.nami.org*
- *www.mhanational.org*
- *www.mentalhealthfirstaid.org*

•••

For those who would like to learn more about the types of mental illnesses, the DSM-V would be a great resource. You can also visit *www.betterhealth.vic.gov.au* and click on the "Mental Health Services" tab under "Services and Support." On that page, there is a webpage titled "Types of Mental Health Issues and Illnesses," which explains the different types of mental health disorders.

•••

Part of fighting the stigma surrounding mental health is normalizing conversations about it in your family! Here are a few websites that provide a great guide on how to do just that:

- *www.aacap.org/AACAP/Families_and_Youth/Facts_for_Families/FFF-Guide/Talking-To-Kids-About-Mental-Illnesses-084.aspx*
- *www.mentalhealth.gov/talk/friends-family-members*
- *www.pta.org/podcast-ARaskin* (This is a podcast, but still an *amazing* resource!)

•••

If you are looking for professional help, specifically a therapist/counselor, psychologist, treatment center, psychiatrist, or a support group, check out *www.psychologytoday.com/us/therapists*. It has a comprehensive directory in which you can change your preferences to find the professional service provider that is the best match for you and what you're looking for.

•••

For those who are looking for something in the virtual world, specifically, an online therapy group, visit *www.healthline.com/health/mental-health/online-group-therapy*. This article goes into great depth about what online therapy groups are, their benefits and limitations, and whether they are right for you. They also recommend ten different online therapy group platforms/organizations.

•••

Also, be sure to check out some of these articles/organizations that list many free online tools available to you!

- *www.oprah.com/omagazine/ free-online-resources-for-mental-illness*
- *www.adolescenthealth.org/Resources/Clinical-Care-Resources/Mental-Health/Mental-Health-Resources-For-Adolesc.aspx*
- *www.counseling.org/knowledge-center/ mental-health-resources*

•••

I hope these resources are helpful to you! If you'd like more information, have any questions, or would like more guidance on navigating the world of mental health, you can always contact me at: *tanaya.business@gmail.com.*

ACKNOWLEDGEMENTS

———

First and foremost, I need to thank my family. Mom, Dad, Adithi—thank you all for your unwavering love and support, for reminding me to eat when I got too caught up with writing, for allowing me to drag my laptop around, for listening to my complaints, for motivating me, for having an open mind, for encouraging me to follow my dreams, for reading through countless versions of my chapters and discussing with me how they could be better. You three have always believed in me and my writing—for that (and more), I will always be grateful. I would not be doing this, I would not be who I am, without you three. I must have done something really good in my past lives to be surrounded by such amazing, inspiring, and loving people like you three. Love you all, eternally.

Next, I must thank Mrs. McCoy. Since high school, you've been a mentor, an inspiration, and a friend to me. You've pushed me to become better and have always guided me toward becoming stronger. Your selflessness will always inspire me. Thank you for painstakingly going through the entirety of my book to help make it better; thank you for helping me reach all my goals, without asking for virtually anything in return. Even in a million years, I could never properly repay you, but I hope you understand the gratitude and the love I hold for you.

Thank you to the individuals featured in my book, for allowing me to hear your stories and share them with the world. I will always be honored and grateful to have had this opportunity to listen to your experiences, to write about your hopes, your dreams, your trials, and your tribulations. The strength you all possess, the vulnerability you all have shown—I am truly in awe. And thank you to the mental health professionals, medical physicians, and medical students of my book for making time in your busy schedules to answer my questions and teach me more about the realities of mental health and mental illness. You are all helping to create a world that is more accepting and more understanding; you are all changing people's lives. Thank you for giving me the opportunity to do the same.

I also want to thank Ramone, Faatima, McCoy, Mom, and Adithi for being my beta readers. I hope this final version makes you proud; it wouldn't have happened without your keen eyes and wonderful suggestions. And, of course, a huge thank you to Sai Seshadri, for helping me develop the book in its initial stages, providing input, and hopping on calls with me to brainstorm how this book could be structured. Thank you to Morgana, my editor, for giving me the encouragement and the tough love needed to make this book a reality.

And finally, a HUGE thank you to my presale campaign supporters, many of whom were friends, friends of friends, family, and even strangers. Without your initial belief in me and my writing, this book would not have been possible.

For this, I must specifically thank Sarah Amir, Paulla Dannug, Sumena Dahal, Mahalakshmi Parakala, Seema

Shaik, Faatima Ali, Edrea Low, Meg Braun, Marco Abbiate, Brent Insua, Vishakha Kanaki, Ormina Naveed, Anjan Aireddy, Atikha Yilayavilli, Zaynab Attaras, Lauren Fletcher, Preethika Rangamgari, Aditi Sen, Sai Bharathula, Zaid Umar, Alex Sliker, Layla Dargahi, Swetha Thiru, Sushmitha Varadha, Aditya Lakkoju, Riyan Pasha, Amy Wong, Darcie Massey, Eman Ghaith, Sawera Haq, Ramone Andrade, Jae Hee Koh, Chloe Paras, Saejel Mohan, Janna Bhatia, Jaice Thomas, Aishani Chauhan, Camille Suliguin, Christina Kilyanek, Kelly Lopez, Sriya Chilukuri, Chinmayi Mutyala, Angela Crisostomo, Jennylyn Patague, Teja Sarraff, Patricia Magpoc, Sameh Shaikh, and Henri Jenoudet—just *some* of my darling, amazing, loving, wonderful friends who've supported me throughout this book journey of mine, even grabbing a copy though we are all broke college students. I am eternally grateful to you all.

Thank you to Professor Donnett Flash for helping me become a better writer and for making me feel welcome on a campus as large as Berkeley. Thank you to my "big sister" Atmanah Parab, the ever-inspirational Jacqueline Azah, Julie Trinh, Shivali Kanwar, Hannah Bittar, Arshita Sandhiparthi, Joe Dangtran, Ihuoma Kanu, and Mahwash Mustafa for being the upperclassmen I could always look up to and rely on. Thank you to Miari Stephens and Jenny DeRuntz from the YWCA—you both have made the Y into a place I'm always thankful to be a part of. Thank you Caitlin Le, Kashish Kharbanda, Susanna Yee, Allison Lai, and Ragini Lal—I'm so happy to have connected with you all during my book-writing process and to be able to call you all my friends! Thank you, Mom, Dad, Adithi, Chetana Mami, Pavan Mama, and Thatha (Ramchander Jagirdar) for supporting me. Thank you Mr. Charles Schallhorn, for educating me about the world of mental health and supporting me in high school as our NAMI advisor. Thank you, Mrs. Nicole Gary, Professor Mary Kelsey, Mrs. Barbara Rogers, Mrs. Elaine Eidam, Mr. Francisco Soto, Mrs. Donna Earle, Mrs. Elizabeth Qutob, Mrs. Mary Lindsey, Mr. Nic Lasnier, and Mr. Edward Plaksa for supporting me throughout my academic, educational, personal, and writing journey; you all have helped shape me into who I am today, teaching me what it means to be a good human and about the world around me. Because of you all, I have a deep love of learning—so, from the bottom of my heart, thank you. Thank you to my fellow Noodle, Miguel Cortes, for getting a copy.

Thank you to Subramanyam Posa, Elizabeth Lamanna, Angelique Marie, Kayla West, Eric Koester, Srinivasa Bittla, Sheelah Bearfoot, Shanay Price, Kirk Hlavka, Nia Sanders, Mamatha Pooskur, Aleeza Khan, Satishbabu Paladugula, Gorky Kumaresan, Manjit Dokal, Teya Khalil, Helen Chan, Sai Seshadri, Leah Arthur, Jennifer Leo, Meera Rao, Samantha Sebandal, Jonathon Daniell, Mena Parmar, Allison Peck, Stephanie Kim, Lydia Mazze, and Divya Prakash.

Thank you to my anonymous donor, who I may never know the identity of but will always be thankful for. You didn't just help me reach and exceed my presale campaign goal—you helped fund my dreams.

Thank you *all* for your contributions and for helping me reach my presale campaign goal. I hope this book makes each and every one of you proud. I truly am lucky to have such caring, supportive people around me.

APPENDIX

INTRODUCTION

Centers for Disease Control and Prevention. "Adolescent Health." National Center for Health Statistics. Last modified April 14, 2021. *https://www.cdc.gov/nchs/fastats/adolescent-health.htm.*

Centers for Disease Control and Prevention. "10 Leading Causes of Death by Age Group, United States- 2018." National Center for Injury Prevention and Control. Web Based Injury Statistics Query and Reporting System (WISQARS). 2018. Accessed January 4, 2021. *http://www.cdc.gov/injury/wisqars/index.html.*

Hijioka, Shihoko, and Joel Wong. "Suicide Among Asian Americans." American Psychological Association. 2012. Accessed December 2, 2020. *https://www.apa.org/pi/oema/resources/ethnicity-health/asian-american/suicide.*

Mental Health America. "Asian American/Pacific Islander Communities And Mental Health." 2021. Accessed November 14, 2020. *https://www.mhanational.org/issues/asian-americanpacific-islander-communities-and-mental-health.*

United States Department of Health and Human Services, Office of Minority Health. "Mental and Behavioral Health- Asian Americans." Last modified May 19, 2021. *https://minorityhealth. hhs.gov/omh/browse.aspx?lvl=4&lvlid=54.*

United States Department of Health and Human Services, Substance Abuse and Mental Health Services Administration. *2018 National Survey on Drug Use and Health: Asians/Native Hawaiians and Other Pacific Islanders (NHOPI).* 2018. *https:// www.samhsa.gov/data/sites/default/files/reports/rpt23248/3_ Asian_NHOPI_2020_01_14.pdf.*

CHAPTER 1: A BRIEF BACKGROUND ON MENTAL HEALTH

Abhyankar, Ravi. "Psychiatric Thoughts in Ancient India." *Mens Sana Monographs* 13, no. 1 (January-December 2015): 59–69. doi:10.4103/0973-1229.153304.

American Psychiatric Association. *Diagnostic and statistical manual of mental disorders: DSM-5.* Arlington, VA: American Psychiatric Association, 2013.

American Psychiatric Association. "DSM-5: Frequently Asked Questions." Feedback and Questions. 2013. Accessed November 3, 2020. *https://www.psychiatry.org/psychiatrists/practice/dsm/ feedback-and-questions/frequently-asked-questions.*

American Psychiatric Association. "Elimination Disorders." DSM Library. 2014. Accessed November 3, 2020. *https://doi. org/10.1176/appi.books.9780890425596.dsm11.*

American Psychological Association. "Patient Health Questionnaire (PHQ-9 & PHQ-2)." Last modified June 2020. *https:// www.apa.org/pi/about/publications/caregivers/practice-settings/ assessment/tools/patient-health.*

Andrew, Evan. "7 Unusual Ancient Medical Techniques." *History. com*, August 22, 2018. *https://www.history.com/news/7-unusual-ancient-medical-techniques*.

Brown, George R. "Overview of Paraphilic Disorders." Merck Manual Professional Version. 2021. Last reviewed April 2021. *https://www.merckmanuals.com/professional/psychiatric-disorders/sexuality,-gender-dysphoria,-and-paraphilias/overview-of-paraphilic-disorders?redirectid=10#:~:text=Paraphilic%20disorders%20are%20recurrent%2C%20intense,the%20potential%20to%20cause%20harm*.

Casarella, Jennifer. "Types of Mental Illness." WebMD. 2021. Accessed December 30, 2020. *https://www.webmd.com/mental-health/mental-health-types-illness#2*.

Cherry, Kendra. "A List of Psychological Disorders." Verywell Mind. Last modified March 19, 2020. *https://www.verywellmind. com/a-list-of-psychological-disorders-2794776*.

Chiang, Howard. *Psychiatry and Chinese History*. London: Pickering & Chatto, 2014.

Faris, Stephanie. "Is Depression Genetic?" Healthline. Last modified April 5, 2021. *https://www.healthline.com/health/depression/genetic#:~:text=The%20depression%20gene&text=The%20chromosome%203p25%2D26%20was,up%20the%20other%20 60%20percent*.

Foley, Dianna. "DSM-5 vs. ICD-10-CM." *Journal of AHIMA*, August 10, 2016. *https://journal.ahima.org/dsm-5-vs-icd-10-cm/*.

Kang Chetna. "Hinduism and Mental Health: Engaging British Hindus." *Mental Health, Religion & Culture* 13, no. 6 (September 2010): 587–93. doi:10.1080/13674676.2010.488427.

Lexico.com. s.v. "mental health." 2021. Accessed November 18, 2020. *https://www.lexico.com/en/definition/mental_health.*

Mancine, Ryley. "Horror Movies and Mental Health Conditions Through the Ages." *The American Journal of Psychiatry* 16, no. 1 (September 2020): 17-17. *https://doi.org/10.1176/appi. ajp-rj.2020.160110.*

Mayo Clinic Staff. "Female Sexual Dysfunction: Symptoms & Causes." Mayo Clinic. 2020. Accessed November 3, 2020. *https://www.mayoclinic.org/diseases-conditions/female-sex-ual-dysfunction/symptoms-causes/syc-20372549#:~:tex-t=Persistent%2C%20recurrent%20problems%20with%20 sexual,known%20medically%20as%20sexual%20dysfunction.*

Mayo Clinic Staff. "Gender Dysphoria: Symptoms & Causes." Mayo Clinic. 2019a. Accessed November 3, 2020. *https://www. mayoclinic.org/diseases-conditions/gender-dysphoria/symp-toms-causes/syc-20475255#:~:text=Gender%20dysphoria%20 is%20the%20feeling,some%20point%20in%20their%20lives.*

Mayo Clinic Staff. "Mental health: What's normal, what's not." Mayo Clinic. 2019b. Accessed January 3, 2021. *https://www. mayoclinic.org/healthy-lifestyle/adult-health/in-depth/men-tal-health/art-20044098.*

Mayo Clinic Staff. "Mental Illness: Diagnosis & Treatment." Mayo Clinic. 2019c. Accessed December 24, 2020. *https://www.may-oclinic.org/diseases-conditions/mental-illness/diagnosis-treat-ment/drc-20374974.*

Mayo Clinic Staff. "Mental Illness: Symptoms & Causes." Mayo Clinic. 2019d. Accessed December 23, 2020. *https://www.may-oclinic.org/diseases-conditions/mental-illness/symptoms-causes/ syc-20374968.*

Mental Health Foundation. "What is good mental health?" 2021. Accessed May 21, 2021. *https://www.mentalhealth.org.uk/your-mental-health/about-mental-health/what-good-mental-health.*

Miller, Sonja. "History of Mental Illness from the Stone Age to the 20th Century." Lumen, Abnormal Psychology. OER Creation. n.d. Accessed June 27, 2021. *https://courses.lumenlearning.com/hvcc-abnormalpsychology/chapter/1-5-prominent-themes-in-abnormal-psychology-throughout-history/.*

Minas, Harry, and Milton Lewis. *Mental Health in Asia and the Pacific: Historical and Cultural Perspectives.* International and Cultural Psychology. New York, NY: Springer, 2017.

Mind Infoline. "Mental health problems- an introduction." 2017. Accessed March 21, 2021. *https://www.mind.org.uk/information-support/types-of-mental-health-problems/mental-health-problems-introduction/causes/.*

Novella, Enric J. "Mental Health Care and the Politics of Inclusion: A Social Systems Account of Psychiatric Deinstitutionalization." *Theoretical Medicine and Bioethics* 31, no. 6 (December 2010): 411-427. doi:10.1007/s11017-010-9155-8.

Pattani, Azeri. "She kept losing her eyesight, and no one knew why. Then a doctor asked about her mental health." *The Philadelphia Inquirer,* January 22, 2019. *https://www.inquirer.com/health/asian-american-mental-illness-somatic-symptoms-diana-chao-20190122.html.*

PBS. "Treatment for Mental Illness." American Experience. n.d. Accessed February 17, 2021. *https://www.pbs.org/wgbh/americanexperience/features/nash-treatments-mental-illness/.*

Peletz, Michael G. "Transgenderism and Gender Pluralism in Southeast Asia since Early Modern Times." *Current Anthropology* 47, no. 2 (April 2006): 309-40. doi:10.1086/498947.

Prins, Seth J. "Does Transinstitutionalization Explain the Over-representation of People with Serious Mental Illnesses in the Criminal Justice System?" *Community Mental Health Journal* 47, no. 6 (December 2011): 716-722.

Queensland Health. *Health Care Providers' Handbook on Hindu Patients.* Division of the Chief Health Officer, Queensland Health. 2011. Accessed on April 4, 2021. *https://www.health.qld.gov.au/__data/assets/pdf_file/0024/156255/hbook-hindu.pdf.*

Samaniego, Réné M. "The Evolution of Psychiatry and Mental Health in the Philippines." *Taiwanese Journal of Psychiatry* 31, no. 2 (2017): 101-114. *https://search.ebscohost.com/login.aspx?direct=true&db=edsarl&AN=edsarl.10283684.201706.201707040025.201707040025.101.114. ii&site=eds-live&authtype=ip,guest&custid=s1226370&groupid=main&profile=eds.*

Tseng, Wen-Shing. "The Development of Psychiatric Concepts in Traditional Chinese Medicine." *Archives of General Psychiatry* 29, no. 4 (October 1973): 569-575. *https://doi.org/10.1001/archpsyc.1973.04200040109018*

Unite for Sight. "Module 2: A Brief History of Mental Illness and the U.S. Mental Health Care System." 2021. Accessed January 20, 2021. *https://www.uniteforsight.org/mental-health/module2.*

Zilboorg, Gregory, and George W. Henry. *A History of Medical Psychology.* New York City, NY: W.W. Norton, 1941.

CHAPTER 2: ASIAN AMERICANS AND MENTAL HEALTH

Ashraf, Anjabeen (@dranjabeenashraf). "I've been mulling over these questions for a while. We are nearing the end of BIPOC Mental Health Month and I've seen some great discussions happening." Instagram photo, July 29, 2020. *https://www.instagram.com/p/CDPLPomjmE3/*

Asian Pacific Institute on Gender-Based Violence. "Census Data & API Identities." 2021. Accessed January 21, 2021. *https://www.api-gbv.org/resources/census-data-api-identities/#:~:text=API%20Ethnicities%20and%20Regional%20Groupings&text=There%20is%20tremendous%20diversity%2C%20with,an%20ethnic%20group%20from%20Laos.*

Budiman, Abby, and Neil G. Ruiz. "Key Facts About Asian Americans, a Diverse and Growing Population." Pew Research Center. 2021a. Accessed October 17, 2020. *https://www.pewresearch.org/fact-tank/2021/04/29/key-facts-about-asian-americans/.*

Budiman, Abby, and Neil G. Ruiz. "Key Facts About Asian Origin Groups in the U.S." Pew Research Center. 2021b. Accessed October 17, 2020. *https://www.pewresearch.org/fact-tank/2021/04/29/key-facts-about-asian-origin-groups-in-the-u-s/.*

Constante, Agnes. "Largest U.S. Refugee Group Struggles with Poverty 45 Years after Resettlement." *NBC News*, March 4, 2020. *https://www.nbcnews.com/news/asian-america/largest-u-s-refugee-group-struggling-poverty-45-years-after-n1150031*

Hansen, Annelie. "The Spirit of Fa'a Samoa: Traditions at the Heart of Samoan Culture." *FamilySearch Blog*, Family Search, April 29, 2020. *https://www.familysearch.org/blog/en/samoan-culture-faa-samoa/.*

History Detectives. "Feature Chinese Immigration." Oregon Public Broadcasting for PBS. 2014. Accessed January 28, 2021. *https://www.pbs.org/opb/historydetectives/feature/chinese-immigration/#:~:text=Chinese%20immigrants%20first%20flocked%20to,Americans%20were%20considered%20cheap%20labor.*

Kiang, Peter N. "Understanding Our Perceptions of Asian Americans." Asia Society Center for Global Education. n.d. Accessed April 1, 2021. *https://asiasociety.org/education/understanding-our-perceptions-asian-americans.*

Kudva, Kundadak Ganesh, Samer El Hayek, Anoop Krishna Gupta, Shunya Kurokawa, Liu Bangshan, Villavicencio, Maria Victoria C. Armas, Kengo Oishi, Saumya Mishra, Saratcha Tiensuntisook, and Norman Sartorius. "Stigma in Mental Illness: Perspective from Eight Asian Nations." *Asia-Pacific Psychiatry* 12, no. 2 (June 2020): 1–10. doi:10.1111/appy.12380.

Minas, Harry, and Hervita Diatri. "*Pasung:* Physical Restraint and Confinement of the Mentally Ill in the Community." *International Journal of Mental Health Symptoms* 2, no. 1 (June 2008): 8. *https://doi.org/10.1186/1752-4458-2-8.*

Odo, Franklin. "Asian Americans and Pacific Islanders in the Making of the Nation." National Park Service. Last modified June 5, 2018. *https://www.nps.gov/articles/asian-americans-and-pacific-islanders-in-the-making-of-the-nation.htm.*

Pew Forum. "Asian Americans: A Mosaic of Faiths." Pew Research Center. 2012. Accessed February 5, 2021. *https://www.pewforum.org/2012/07/19/asian-americans-a-mosaic-of-faiths-overview/.*

Pew Forum. "The Rise of Asian Americans." Pew Research Center. Last modified April 4, 2013. *https://www.pewresearch.org/social-trends/2012/06/19/the-rise-of-asian-americans/.*

PTI. "More than 19,500 Mother Tongues Spoken in India: Census." *The Indian Express,* July 1, 2018. *https://indianexpress.com/article/india/more-than-19500-mother-tongues-spoken-in-india-census-5241056/.*

Sharma, Kriti. "Living in Chains: Shackling of People with Psychosocial Disabilities Worldwide." Human Rights Watch. 2020. *https://www.hrw.org/report/2020/10/06/living-chains/shackling-people-psychosocial-disabilities-worldwide#.*

Tanap, Ryann. "Why Asian-Americans and Pacific Islanders Don't go to Therapy." *NAMI Blog,* NAMI, July 25, 2019. *https://www.*

nami.org/Blogs/NAMI-Blog/July-2019/Why-Asian-Americans-and-Pacific-Islanders-Don-t-go-to-Therapy.

U.S. Department of Health and Human Services, Office of Minority Health. "Profile: Asian Americans." 2021a. Last modified April 5, 2021. *https://minorityhealth.hhs.gov/omh/browse.aspx?lvl=3&lvlid=63.*

U.S. Department of Health and Human Services, Office of Minority Health. "Profile: Native Hawaiians/Pacific Islanders." 2021b. Last modified April 5, 2021. *https://minorityhealth.hhs.gov/omh/browse.aspx?lvl=3&lvlid=65.*

Xie, Angel. "How Does Collectivism Influence Asian Culture." *Medium,* May 21, 2018. *https://angelxie.medium.com/how-does-collectivism-influence-asian-culture-36a1045b884b.*

CHAPTER 3: SARA AHMED

Carberg, Jenna, and Kimberly Langdon. "Postpartum Depression Statistics. Postpartum Depression. 2021. Last modified June 3, 2021. *https://www.postpartumdepression.org/resources/statistics/.*

Centers for Disease Control and Prevention. "Depression Among Women." Reproductive Health. 2020. Accessed January 2, 2021. *https://www.cdc.gov/reproductivehealth/depression/index.htm.*

Healthline Editorial Team, and Julie Lay. "What Bodily Changes Can You Expect During Pregnancy?" Healthline Parenthood. 2017. Accessed January 2, 2021. *https://www.healthline.com/health/pregnancy/bodily-changes-during#hormonal-changes.*

Kim, Lydia. "Psychotherapy with Asian Clients: An Exploratory Study of the Perspectives of East Asian Clinicians." PhD diss., Rutgers University, 2015.

Kraft, David P. "One Hundred Years of College Mental Health." *Journal of American College Health* 59, no. 6 (June/July 2011): 477-81. *https://doi.org/10.1080/07448481.2011.569964.*

Mayo Clinic Staff. "Postpartum Depression: Symptoms & Causes." Mayo Clinic. 2018. Accessed January 2, 2021. *https://www.mayoclinic.org/diseases-conditions/postpartum-depression/symptoms-causes/syc-20376617.*

Serani, Deborah. "Why Consistency Matters in Your Mental Health Plan." *Dr. Deb* (blog), January 13, 2017. *https://drdeborahserani.blogspot.com/2017/01/why-consistency-matters-in-your-mental.html.*

Smith, Melinda, and Jeanne Segal. "Postpartum Depression and the Baby Blues." HelpGuide. Last modified September 2020. *https://www.helpguide.org/articles/depression/postpartum-depression-and-the-baby-blues.htm.*

Sullivan, Cole. "'It's Okay to Need Help': Mom Shares Story of Postpartum Depression." *WBIR Channel 10*, June 12, 2020. *https://www.wbir.com/article/life/family/parenting-101/its-okay-to-need-help-mom-shares-story-of-postpartum-depression/51-d527b4af-5d26-4330-8a58-d95bed2d3fb0.*

Wisner, Katherine L., Dorothy K. Y. Sit, Mary C. McShea, David M. Rizzo, Rebecca A. Zoretich, Carolyn L. Hughes, Heather F. Eng, et al. "Onset Timing, Thoughts of Self-harm, and Diagnoses in Postpartum Women with Screen-Positive Depression Findings." *JAMA Psychiatry* 70, no. 5 (May 2013): 490-498. doi:10.1001/jamapsychiatry.2013.87.

World Health Organization. "Maternal Mental Health." Mental Health and Substance Use. n.d. Accessed January 2, 2021. *https://www.who.int/mental_health/maternal-child/maternal_mental_health/en/.*

CHAPTER 4: JAMES

Encyclopaedia Britannica Online. s.v. "Long Island." Accessed December 14, 2020. https://www.britannica.com/place/Long-Island-New-York.

Anderson, Meg, and Kavitha Cardoza. "Mental Health in Schools: A Hidden Crisis Affecting Millions of Students." *NPR Ed*, August 31, 2016. https://www.npr.org/sections/ed/2016/08/31/464727159/mental-health-in-schools-a-hidden-crisis-affecting-millions-of-students.

Askarinam, Leah, and National Journal. "Schools in Poor Areas Have More Students with Mental Health Needs." *The Atlantic*, January 13, 2016. https://www.theatlantic.com/politics/archive/2016/01/schools-in-poor-areas-have-more-students-with-mental-health-needs/458808/.

Mind Infoline. "Mental health problems- an introduction." 2017. Accessed March 21, 2021. https://www.mind.org.uk/information-support/types-of-mental-health-problems/mental-health-problems-introduction/causes/.

Nadal, Kevin L., and Ford Kuramoto. "A Snapshot of Behavioral Health Issues for Asian American/Native Hawaiian/Pacific Islander Boys and Men: Jumpstarting an Overdue Conversation." Cabezon Group, Inc. for SAMHSA. 2016. Accessed December 14, 2020. https://store.samhsa.gov/sites/default/files/d7/priv/sma16-4959.pdf.

Walker, Tim. "Are Schools Ready to Tackle the Mental Health Crisis?" *neaToday*, September, 13, 2018. https://www.nea.org/advocating-for-change/new-from-nea/are-schools-ready-tackle-mental-health-crisis.

Wallace, Jennifer B. "Students in High-Achieving Schools Are Now Named an 'At-Risk' Group, Study Says." *Washington*

Post, September 26, 2019. *https://www.washingtonpost.com/ lifestyle/2019/09/26/students-high-achieving-schools-are-now-named-an-at-risk-group/*.

CHAPTER 5: HALIMA KHAN

California Department of Education. "Youth Suicide Prevention." 2020. Accessed July 29, 2020. *https://www.cde.ca.gov/ls/cg/mh/ suicideprevres.asp*.

Heron, Melonie. "Deaths: Leading Causes for 2017." *National Vital Statistics Reports* 69, no. 6. Hyattsville, MD: National Center for Health Statistics, 2019. *https://www.cdc.gov/nchs/data/nvsr/ nvsr68/nvsr68_06-508.pdf*.

Hsu, Helen. "Crazy Rich Asians is a Movie; Crazy Asians is a Social Problem." Interview by Emil Guillermo. *Emil Amok's Takeout*, Asian American Legal Defense and Education Fund, November 30, 2018. Audio, 47:12. *https://www.aaldef.org/blog/ podcast-emil-amok-s-takeout-asian-american-and-pacific-is-lander-mental-health-empowerment/*.

Kim, Hee Jun, EunMi Park, Carla L. Storr, Katherine Tran, and Hee-Soon Juan. "Depression Among Asian-American Adults in the Community: Systematic Review and Meta-Analysis." *PLoS ONE* 10, no. 6 (June 2015): e0127760. doi:10.1371/journal. pone.0127760.

Mental Health America. "Asian American/Pacific Islander Communities and Mental Health." 2021. Accessed November 14, 2020. *https://www.mhanational.org/issues/asian-americanpa-cific-islander-communities-and-mental-health*.

NAMI. "Are There Any Online Resources for Therapy/Support Groups or Mental Health Apps?" NAMI Online Knowledge Center. n.d. Accessed May 1, 2021. *https://nami.zendesk.com/*

hc/en-us/articles/360024615074-Are-there-any-online-resources-for-therapy-support-groups-or-mental-health-apps-.

NAMI Multicultural and International Outreach Center. "Asian American and Pacific Islander Communities (AA/PIs) Mental Health Facts." 2003. Accessed July 29, 2020. *https://www.naminys.org/images/uploads/pdfs/Asian%20American%20Disparities%20in%20Mental%20Health%20Care.pdf.*

Narayanan, H. S., K. S. Mohan, and V.K. Radhakrishnan. "The Karma Theory of Mental Illness." *NIMHANS Journal* 4, no. 1 (January 1986): 61–63. *https://nimhans.ac.in/wp-content/uploads/2020/10/9.-The-Karma-Theory-of-Mental-Illness_61-63.pdf.*

National Institute of Mental Health. "Depression." Mental Health Information. 2018. Accessed November 14, 2020. *https://www.nimh.nih.gov/health/topics/depression/.*

National Institute of Mental Health. "Major Depression." Mental Health Information. 2019. Accessed November 14, 2020. *https://www.nimh.nih.gov/health/statistics/major-depression.*

Quinn, Cristina. "Mass. Study Shows Major Mental Healthcare Disparity Between Whites and Asian-Americans." *GBH News,* April 25, 2018. *https://www.wgbh.org/news/2018/04/25/news/mass-study-shows-major-mental-healthcare-disparity-between-whites-and-asian.*

CHAPTER 6: SONYA

Hubbard, Kathy. "Binge-eating disorder is a serious mental health issue." n.d. Accessed February 20, 2021. *https://www.bonner-general.org/binge-eating-disorder-serious-mental-health-issue/.*

National Eating Disorder Association. "Binge Eating Disorder."
n.d. Accessed February 20, 2021. *https://www.nationaleating-disorders.org/learn/by-eating-disorder/bed.*

CHAPTER 7: MIRABELLE LEI

American Psychiatric Association Division of Diversity and Health
Equity. *Mental Health Disparities: LGBTQ.* 2017. Accessed
March 3, 2021. *https://www.psychiatry.org/File%20Library/
Psychiatrists/Cultural-Competency/Mental-Health-Disparities/
Mental-Health-Facts-for-LGBTQ.pdf.*

Ching, Terence H.W., Sharon Y. Lee, Julia Chen, Rachel P. So, and
Monnica T. Williams. "A Model of Intersectional Stress and
Trauma in Asian American Sexual and Gender Minorities."
Psychology of Violence 8, no. 6 (November 2018): 657-668.
https://doi.org/10.1037/vi00000204.

Cleveland Clinic. "Body Dysmorphic Disorder." Health Library.
2020. Accessed March 3, 2021. *https://my.clevelandclinic.org/
health/diseases/9888-body-dysmorphic-disorder.*

Mayo Clinic Staff. "Body Dysmorphic Disorder: Symptoms &
Causes." Mayo Clinic. 2019. Accessed March 3, 2021. *https://
www.mayoclinic.org/diseases-conditions/body-dysmorphic-dis-order/symptoms-causes/syc-20353938.*

Min, Pyong G. "Koreans' Immigration to the U.S: History and
Contemporary Trends." Queens, NY: The Research Center for
Korean Community, 2011. *https://www.qc.cuny.edu/Academics/
Centers/RCKC/Documents/Koreans%20Immigration%20to%20
the%20US.pdf.*

Monsoon Asians and Pacific Islanders in Solidarity. "Asians in
Iowa." n.d. Accessed March 3, 2021. *https://monsooniowa.org/
asians-in-iowa/.*

Saghir, Sheedba, and Lynda Hyland. "The Effects of Immigration and Media Influence on Body Image Among Pakistani Men." *Am J Men's Health* 11, no. 4 (July 2017): 930-940. doi: 10.1177/1557988317698627.

Stepanova, Elena V., and Michael J. Strube. "What's in a Face? The Role of Skin Tone, Facial Physiognomy, and Color Representation Mode of Facial Primes in Affective Priming Effects." *The Journal of Social Psychology* 152, no. 2 (January 2012): 212-227. *https://doi.org/10.1080/00224545.2011.597797.*

Sutter, Megan, and Paul B. Perrin. "Discrimination, Mental Health, and Suicidal Ideation Among LGBTQ People of Color." *Journal of Counseling Psychology* 63, no.1 (January 2016): 98-105. *https://doi.org/10.1037/cou0000126.*

The Trevor Project. "Asian/Pacific Islander LGBTQ Youth Mental Health." 2020. Accessed March 3, 2021. *https://www.thetrevorproject.org/2020/05/13/research-brief-asian-pacific-islander-lgbtq-youth-mental-health/.*

CHAPTER 8: TYSON

Alcohol and Drug Foundation. "Depressants." Drug Facts. 2021. Accessed March 13, 2021. *https://adf.org.au/drug-facts/depressants/.*

Casarella, Jennifer. "Types of Bipolar Disorder." WebMD. 2021. Accessed March 12, 2021. *https://www.webmd.com/bipolar-disorder/guide/bipolar-disorder-forms.*

Disken, Even. "The Beauty and Pain of the Pe'a, the Traditional Samoan Tattoo." Matador Network. 2020. Accessed March 12, 2021. *https://matadornetwork.com/read/traditional-samoan-tattoo/.*

Hilliard, Jena. "Is Alcohol a Depressant?" Addiction Center. Last modified June 16, 2021. *https://www.addictioncenter.com/alcohol/is-alcohol-a-depressant/*.

Kim, Dahyeon. "Too Well-Off to Seek Help? The Model Minority Myth of Asian Americans." *ADAA Professional Blogs*, Anxiety & Depression Association of America, April 1, 2021. Accessed March 12, 2021. *https://adaa.org/learn-from-us/from-the-experts/blog-posts/professional/too-well-seek-help-model-minority-myth-asian*.

Lesser, Ben. "Connection Between Substance Use Disorder and Mental Illness." DualDiagnosis.org. 2021. Last modified May 25, 2021. *https://dualdiagnosis.org/mental-health-and-addiction/the-connection/*.

Mayo Clinic Staff. "Bipolar Disorder: Symptoms & Causes." Mayo Clinic. 2021. Accessed March 12, 2021. *https://www.mayoclinic.org/diseases-conditions/bipolar-disorder/symptoms-causes/syc-20355955*.

Mental Health America. "Asian American/Pacific Islander Communities and Mental Health." 2021. Accessed November 14, 2020. *https://www.mhanational.org/issues/asian-americanpacific-islander-communities-and-mental-health*.

National Institute on Drug Abuse. "Part 1: The Connection Between Substance Use Disorders and Mental Illness." In *Common Comorbidities with Substance Use Disorders Research Report*. 2021. Accessed January 21, 2021. *https://www.drugabuse.gov/publications/research-reports/common-comorbidities-substance-use-disorders/part-1-connection-between-substance-use-disorders-mental-illness*.

Pendulum: Stories and Information (blog), Bipolar UK. "Managing Grief in Bipolar Disorder." February 12, 2020. Accessed March

12, 2021. *https://www.bipolaruk.org/blog/managing-grief-in-bi-polar-disorder.*

Rogers Behavioral Health (blog), Rogers Behavioral Health. "Mental Health Stigma: Like Parent, Like Child." September 10, 2015. Accessed March 12, 2021. *https://rogersbh.org/about-us/news-room/blog/mental-health-stigma-parent-child.*

United States Department of Health and Human Services, Substance Abuse and Mental Health Services Administration. *2018 National Survey on Drug Use and Health: Asians/Native Hawaiians and Other Pacific Islanders (NHOPI).* 2018. *https://www.samhsa.gov/data/sites/default/files/reports/rpt23248/3_Asian_NHOPI_2020_01_14.pdf.*

CHAPTER 9: SUSANNA YEE

Good Therapy. "What is Therapy?" Learn About Therapy. 2015. Accessed November 20, 2021. *https://www.goodtherapy.org/what-is-therapy.html.*

Mental Health America. "Asian American/Pacific Islander Communities And Mental Health." 2021. Accessed November 14, 2020. *https://www.mhanational.org/issues/asian-americanpacific-islander-communities-and-mental-health.*

Person, Nadia. "Who Needs Counseling? 10 Therapy Myths Dispelled." *PsychCentral,* May 17, 2016. Accessed April 7, 2021. *https://psychcentral.com/lib/who-needs-counseling-10-therapy-myths-dispelled#6.*

CHAPTER 10: CAITLIN LE

Anxiety & Depression Association of America. "Facts and Statistics." 2021. Accessed December 21, 2021. *https://adaa.org/understanding-anxiety/facts-statistics.*

Bridges to Recovery. "High-Functioning Anxiety." n.d. Accessed December 18, 2020. *https://www.bridgestorecovery.com/ high-functioning-anxiety/.*

Mayo Clinic Staff. "Anxiety Disorders: Symptoms & Causes." Mayo Clinic. 2018. Accessed December 19, 2020. *https://www. mayoclinic.org/diseases-conditions/anxiety/symptoms-causes/ syc-20350961.*

Mayo Clinic Staff. "Mental Illness: Symptoms & Causes." Mayo Clinic. 2019. Accessed December 23, 2020. *https://www.may-oclinic.org/diseases-conditions/mental-illness/symptoms-causes/ syc-20374968.*

Mental Health Center @ DH. "High Functioning Mental Health Disorders." *Depression & Mental Health Blog*, Mental Health Center at Destination Hope, July 5, 2017. Accessed December 19, 2020. *https://www.mentalhealthcenter.org/high-function-ing-mental-health-disorders/.*

National Institute of Mental Health. "Generalized Anxiety Disor-der: When Worry Gets Out of Control." Mental Health Infor-mation. 2016. Accessed December 22, 2021. *https://www.nimh. nih.gov/health/publications/generalized-anxiety-disorder-gad/.*

Tartakovsky, Margarita. "Discontinuing Psychiatric Medications: What You need to Know." *PsychCentral*, May 17, 2016. Accessed December 20, 2020. *https://psychcentral.com/lib/discontinu-ing-psychiatric-medications-what-you-need-to-know#1.*

YoungMinds' Blog, YoungMinds. "Living with a High Functioning Mental Illness." March 7, 2019. Accessed December 17, 2020. *https://youngminds.org.uk/blog/living-with-a-high-functioning-mental-illness/.*

Made in the USA
Coppell, TX
12 June 2024

33459323R00138